■SCHOLASTIC

create and display

Mathematics

Full of exciting activities and displays for the whole curriculum

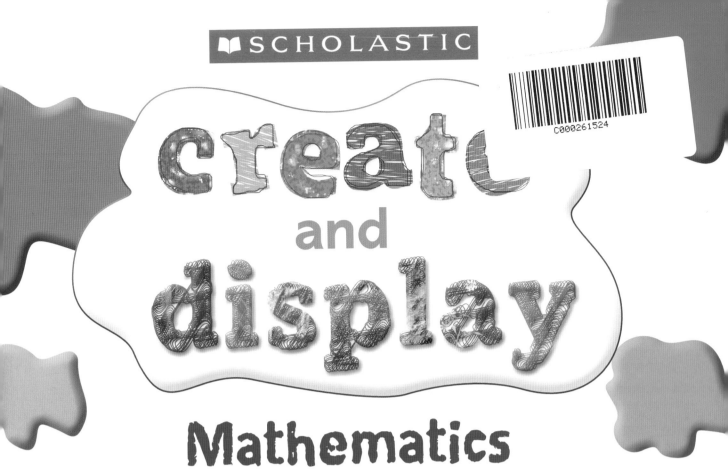

Ages 4-11
for all primary years

Liz Webster and Sue Reed

Book End, Range Road, Witney, Oxfordshire, OX29 OYD
www.scholastic.co.uk

© 2011, Scholastic Ltd

1 2 3 4 5 6 7 8 9   0 1 2 3 4 5 6 7 8 9

British Library Cataloguing-in-Publication Data
A catalogue record for this book is available from the
British Library.

ISBN 978-1407-12525-1
Printed by Bell & Bain Ltd, Glasgow

Text © 2011 Scholastic Education on behalf of
the authors

Commissioning Editor
Paul Naish

Development Editor
Emily Jefferson

Editor
Kate Greig

Series Designer
Andrea Lewis

Designer
Mark Bryan

Photography:
Steve Forrest

Acknowledgements

The authors and publishers would like to thank
the children of Aldingbourne Primary School for
their enthusiasm, hard work and cooperation in
the making of this book. Liz Webster, Headteacher
of Aldingbourne Primary School and her Deputy
Headteacher Sue Reed would like to thank all of
their staff for their cooperation and continued
support. They would like to especially thank Wendy
Davies and Kath Herbert for their hard work and
commitment to helping put this book together. Liz
Webster would like to say a huge thanks to her fab
sister, Georgina Ridehalgh, who has spent hours
inspiring us with lots of new and exciting art ideas.
Sue Reed would like to express a special thanks
to her husband Ollie for his never-ending support.
Finally, they would like to thank Steve Forrest,
the photographer, for being absolutely gorgeous
and always smiling during some very tricky photo
shoots. A big thanks to everybody!

Contents

Introduction

Welcome to *Create and Display: Mathematics*. This book aims to show how Mathematics in primary schools can be taught and displayed in a creative, stimulating and fun way. By displaying Mathematics work in your classroom and school environment, you are highlighting its importance. Throughout this book, we aim to demonstrate how to use display so that it is a valuable tool to enhance children's learning, to improve the quality of teaching for learning and to enrich the classroom environment.

Throughout the book we demonstrate that the most effective Maths lessons are practical and exciting for the children. Each chapter offers a range of stimulating and original ideas that we use in our own classrooms – so we know they work! Each chapter relates to the National Curriculum or Early Years Foundation Stage and can be differentiated to suit different ages and abilities.

The emphasis within this book is not to produce written work but rather to engage children in practical activities with their peers and to play fun and exciting games that will reinforce their learning and leave them wanting more! Every theme in this book follows the same basic structure by including a whole-class starter, practical ideas, art and display ideas and cross-curricular links.

Whole-class Starter

This is the starting point for each theme and to engage the children it must be exciting, stimulating and meaningful.

- In this book a wide range of the lessons have included 'teacher in role', as a teaching strategy. This is a perfect way to capture the children's interest and fire their imaginations.
- An effective teaching strategy that is used repeatedly in this book is 'chatting chums'. This involves the children sharing ideas with a friend before sharing those ideas with the whole class. It acts as a support for less confident children as they may sound out their ideas before expressing their thoughts to the larger group. It ensures that all the children in the class get involved.
- Interactive games as part of the whole-class starter ensure that all learners and learning styles are catered for. The use of movement and action as part of a whole-class starter keeps the children's attention and helps to reinforce their learning.
- Visual props are a vital part of the whole-class starter, but they must be big, bold and colourful.

Art and Display Ideas

- We truly believe that bright, colourful and purposeful displays make a difference to the children's learning as well as enhancing the classroom environment. Children enjoy using their imagination and practical skills. The use of art as a tool encourages them to explore and experiment with different media as well as extending their learning by exploring cross-curricular links.

Cross-curricular Links

- Exploring natural links to other subjects makes learning more relevant and meaningful to young children. In this book we have highlighted ways in which these links might be possible in curriculum areas such as Science, Literacy, ICT, Maths, Design and Technology, and Music.

  Above all Numeracy should be:
  Never dull
  Understandable
  Meaningful
  Energetic
  Relevant
  Active
  Creative
  Yippee! Numeracy is fun!

  We hope this book will help you to enjoy teaching Mathematics as much as the children will enjoy their learning!

  Liz Webster and Sue Reed

Practical Activities

- This part of the lesson reinforces the learning that has taken place during the whole-class starter session and it is vital that it is equally exciting.
- Children love playing games as they actively engage the children and encourage them to be excited about their learning. Therefore we have included ideas for table-top games, carpet games and large-area games.

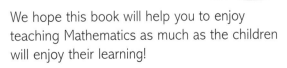

The Count of Number

Whole-class Starter

- Enter the classroom as 'The Count of Number'. This character is similar to the character on *Sesame Street*® called the Count. Start counting forwards and backwards to 10. Explain to the children that you love numbers and you love to count. Encourage the children to help you count forwards and backwards to 10. On your cloak there should be a mixture of numbers and letters. Ask the children to help you sort the numbers from the letters. Place the numbers on the board and the letters in the bin. The children help to put the numbers in the correct order and they all re-count the numbers forwards and backwards.

Focus of Learning
To be able to recognise numbers up to 10

- Use the IWB to help the children develop their skills in counting objects to 10. Using the theme of bats and vampires, prepare a presentation in which different pictures flash up on the screen for the children to count. The children count the objects and the appropriate number will then appear on the board. Encourage the children to come out and write the correct number on the board or hold up the number using number fans.
- Play 'The Counter'. Make a set of laminated cards that have a different number of bats on them. Sit the children in a large circle and in the middle place ten hoops with the numbers 1 to 10 in them. Give each child a card. The object of the game is for each child to count the number of bats on their card and then place the card in the correct hoop.

Practical Activities

- Play 'Haunted Hunt'. Make a set of large haunted houses with numbers 1 to 10 on them and place them around the hall or large space. Make a set of cards with pictures of bats, spiders, skeletons and so on. for the children to count. Give each a child a card for them to try to locate which house it belongs in. For example, a card showing six bats belongs in house number 6, and a card showing eight skeletons belongs in house number 8.

- Play 'Count's Castle'. The object of this game is to get to the Count's castle by crossing on the stepping stones. Make a set of stepping stones with numbers 1 to 10 on one side and the same number of bats on the other side. For this game you could make a castle then place the stepping stones leading to the castle. The children take it in turns to jump on the stepping stones and identify the number in order to move on. If they are correct they turn the stone over and move to the next stone. If they are incorrect they go to the back of the line!

- Play 'Bat Splat'. Display a prepared board on an IWB with numbers 0 to 10 on each bat. Split the children into two teams and choose one person from each team to sit on a chair with their back to the board, holding a fly swatter. Call out a number and the children must race to splat the appropriate bat.

Art and Display Ideas

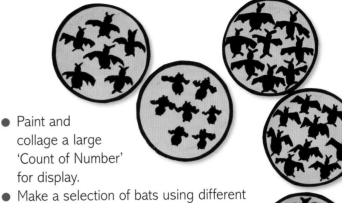

- Paint and collage a large 'Count of Number' for display.

- Make a selection of bats using different media. Demonstrate how to use each media. Discuss with the children their different choices and allow them to choose a medium for their bat.

- Make 3D papier mâché spiders to use for display. Add concertina legs and goggle eyes.

- Using a thick black marker pen, trace over a Celtic-patterned bat to develop hand control skills.

- Use an ICT package and ask the children to create a Celtic-style bat.

- Make a human number line and photograph it for display.

- Chalk pastel moons and paint bats on them to represent the numbers 1 to 10.

Cross-curricular Links

- **Literacy** – Share Jan Pienkowski's *Haunted House* (Walker Books, 2005) and Helen Nicholl's and Jan Pienkowski's *Meg and Mog* (Puffin Books, 2007) with the children. The children should use ideas from the illustrations to recreate their own silhouette picture based on the Count's castle.

- **Music** – Adapt existing number songs so that they are related to your vampire/bat theme and sing with the children. For example, '10 Green Bottles' could become '10 Black Bats'.

- **Physical Development** – Make a set of hand control cards that encourage hand control either by joining the dots or following a maze to match numbers to objects or pictures.

- **Knowledge and Understanding of the World** – Learn facts about bats and spiders.

Order Order!

Whole-class Starter

Focus of Learning
To be able to put numbers in order

- Set up the classroom or large area so it resembles a courtroom with a desk and a gavel. Enter the classroom as a judge. Demand order in the classroom by bashing your gavel on the desk. Sit at the desk and tell the children that today in your courtroom there must be order because without order there is chaos and you have noticed that some numbers have been causing chaos because they are not in the correct order. Reveal a set of consecutive numbers on the IWB which are in the wrong order. Bang the gavel and shout, 'Order order!' Ask the children if they can put the numbers in the correct order. Show them the numbers in the correct order and together they can count to check. Repeat this activity and extend to numbers that are not consecutive, for example 3, 9, 12, 7, 1. This extension will depend on the children's ability.
- Play 'Innocent or Guilty?' The judge explains to the children that some of the numbers that visit her courtroom are naughty numbers, but some have been falsely accused. It is her job to sort out the naughty numbers from the good numbers. Can they help her? Give each child a paddle which on one side has a happy face and on the other side has a sad face. The judge then displays a set of numbers. If they are in the correct order the children should hold up their happy face, but if they are in the wrong order they should hold up their sad face. The judge will then ask the children to help her put them in the right order.
- Play 'Courtroom Chaos'. Make sets of number cards in different colours so that there is enough for one card per child. The children should walk around the classroom and when the judge bangs her gavel and shouts, 'Order order!' they should find the other children in the classroom that have the same colour cards as them and then put their cards in the right order. The judge then asks each group in turn to stand up and read their numbers in the correct order.

Practical Activities

- Play 'Order Order!' Make each child a board with a judge's head on and spaces to fit five numbers. Out of a bag the children pick five numbers and place them on their board. The judge bangs the gavel and shouts, 'Order order!' and the children must put their numbers in the correct order as quickly as possible. The first person to order their numbers correctly is the winner.

- Play 'Sieve and Sequence'. Place a large selection of plastic number tiles in a sandpit. Ask each child from the group to sieve for a tile and place it on a board. Once all the children have placed their numbers on the board the judge shouts, 'Order order!' and the children must write the numbers in the correct order on a whiteboard.

- Play 'The Number Robber'. Make lots of sets of laminated number lines that have numbers missing, stolen by the Number Robber. The children must work out which numbers have been stolen from the correct order and replace them by writing them in.

- Make a selection of dot-to-dots for the children to complete. As an extension the children could draw their own picture and make their own dot-to-dot.

Art and Display Ideas

- Paint and collage a large judge for display.
- Make a giant class number line for display. The children can use oil pastels to decorate the numbers.
- Each child should make their own number line using newspaper, wrapping paper and so on. Laminate the number lines and use them as a teaching aid.
- Using the style of the art movement Vorticism, the children should draw numbers and put them in order.

Cross-curricular Links

- **Literacy** – Learn about alphabetical order.
- **PSHCE** – Talk about right and wrong and the reasons for rules. Discuss with the children your school and classroom rules. What happens if you break the rules?
- **ICT** – Use a programmable toy, for example Bee-Bot™, to teach the importance of programming instructions in the correct order to make the toy function in the correct way.

Adding Adders

Whole-class Starter

- Prepare an IWB presentation. Introduce the children to your friend Adder. Explain that Adder is a snake and he loves to add numbers together. Ask the children if anybody knows what adding means? On the IWB show the children a picture of two snakes with an addition sign in the middle. Each snake has a different amount of dots on it. Explain what the addition sign means and show the children how to read the sum. The children should count the dots on each snake and add them together. Repeat this several times together and then encourage the children to try to add the dots on their own.

- Show the children snakes with numbers on and ask the children how they could add these numbers together. Show the children a strategy that they could use: Two snakes appear on the board, each with a number

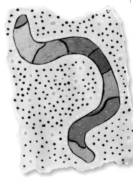

Focus of Learning
To begin to understand how to add two numbers together

on. Show the children how to count out the numbers using their fingers and then count how many fingers altogether to find the answer. Repeat this several times and encourage the children to begin to work independently.

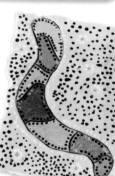

- Play 'Adding Adders'. Make a set of laminated boards with ten snakes on numbered 1 to 10. Give each child, or pair, a board and a pen. On the IWB show the children an adding adder sum on two snakes. The children work out the addition sum and circle the correct snake on their board. For example, 2 + 3 = 5, the children would circle the snake that had the number 5 written on. This could be extended to adding three numbers together.

Practical Activities

- Play 'Snake Pit'. Make a set of laminated snakes with sums on. Place lots of baskets around the classroom or large open space. Place numbers on the baskets that correspond with the answers on the snake sums. The children pick out a sum and work out the answer. They must then either throw or place a toy snake in the correct basket.

- Play 'Solving Snakes'. Make a large number of laminated snakes with addition sums on. Make sure these snakes have a large tongue for the answer. Place the snakes in a basket and place it in the middle of the table. Using a giant egg-timer give the children one minute to answer as many snake sums as possible. Check the answers with the children.

- Play 'Beware the Square'. Make a set of laminated boards that have 20 squares on them, also include start and finish squares (based on 'Snakes and Ladders', but without ladders). On some of the squares place a picture of a snake pit. Make a set of laminated snakes with sums on. The children take it in turns to pick out a snake. The children answer the sum and whatever the answer they move their counter (which could be a snake) that number of squares. If they land on a snake pit square they must return to the start.

Art and Display Ideas

- Create the title 'Adding Adders' using paper plates. Ask the children to use different media to colour, paint or collage the plate. Place a different cut-out letter on each plate. Arrange the plates on the board to resemble a snake.
- Create Aboriginal snake art using paint, oil pastels, cotton buds and tea-stained paper.
- Use felt, fabric and cotton to create a snake picture. Use felt for the background.
- Use watercolour paint to create a background and print a snake on the background using sponges, potatoes and so on.

Cross-curricular Links

- **ICT** – Using Medusa as a stimulus, photograph each child's face and print and cut out the face without the hair. Insert the picture into a paint package. Ask the children to draw lots of differently shaped snakes on to the face to create Medusa snake hair.

- **Personal, Social and Emotional Development** – Play the board game 'Snakes and Ladders' promoting taking turns, sharing and number recognition.
- **History** – Retell the story of Medusa. Who was she and what was her story? Discuss whether she was good or evil.
- **Science** – Learn about snakes and other reptiles.

The Very Hungry Caterpillar

Focus of Learning
To learn the names for the days of the week and learn to sequence them correctly

Whole-class Starter

- Read and enjoy the story of *The Very Hungry Caterpillar* by Eric Carle (Puffin Books, 2002). Discuss with the children the days of the week featured in the book. On the IWB ask the children to match the correct day of the week to the food eaten by the Very Hungry Caterpillar.

- In role as the Very Hungry Caterpillar, you are confused about what food you can eat because you know you can eat oranges on Friday and apples on Monday, but which day comes first and which day comes after that? You just don't know! Can the children help you learn the days of the week? Produce a set of giant flash cards and ask the children to help you read them and put them in the correct order. With your help the children can read, chant or sing the days of the week in the correct order.

- Using the flash cards play 'Disappearing Days'. Place the cards on the board and ask the children to close their eyes. Remove one or two of the cards. Ask the children to open their eyes and identify which days of the week have disappeared. More able children could be encouraged to write on a whiteboard the day of the week that is missing. Repeat this activity but without the cards. The caterpillar chants the days but leaves one out. Which one is missing?

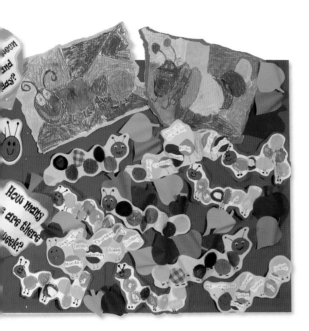

week and place them in the correct order.

- Play 'Crawling Caterpillars'. Use the large cards from the starter session. Place these around a large classroom area or outside area. Give each child a pair of caterpillar deely-boppers. This game could be played in several ways according to the ability of the children:
  1) Call out a day of the week and the caterpillar must crawl to that day.
  2) Chant the days of the week with one missing and the caterpillar must crawl to the missing day.
  3) Make a set of cards that have questions/statements written on them, *What is the day after Monday?, Monday is the day before Tuesday...* The caterpillar must crawl to the correct day of the week.

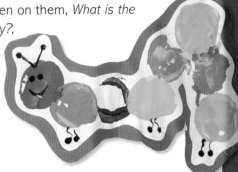

Practical Activities

- Play 'Match a Day'. Make a board with the days of the week on leaf shapes for each child in the group. Make a set of cards in leaf shapes with the days of the week written on. Include some cards with a picture of the Very Hungry Caterpillar. The children take it in turns to pick out a card and try to match it to a leaf on their board. If they pull out the Very Hungry Caterpillar they must remove all the cards they have collected.

- Play 'Winning Week'. Make a set of leaf-shaped cards with a day of the week on each card. Each child needs a complete set of cards. Put all the cards in a bag. Each child takes it in turn to pick out a card. The object of the game is to collect all seven days of the

Art and Display Ideas

- Collage caterpillars using different shades of green.
- Print a caterpillar using different shades of green mixed by the children.
- Colour-mix seven shades of green and paint each segment of his body a different shade of green. Add on the days of the week.

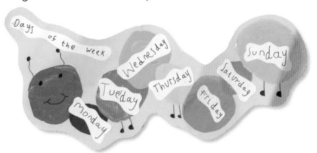

Cross-curricular Links

- **Art** – Paint a caterpillar in the style of Fauvism.
- **D&T** – Make an egg-box caterpillar using recyclable materials.
- **Science** – Learn about the life cycle of a butterfly. Buy some baby caterpillars and watch them grow first hand. Alternatively find videos of hatching butterflies and caterpillars online.

13

Rainbow Riches

Whole-class Starter

- A tiny letter arrives from Larry the Leprechaun. He explains that he is going to help the children learn all about money. He tells the children that he knows all about coins because at the end of his rainbow is a tree with a gold pot full of coins. He invites the children to visit his money tree. Outside the classroom have a prepared tree with lots of money hanging off the leaves and a gold pot full of coins. The children should visit the tree, examine each coin and discuss its properties, for example colour, shape, pictures, numbers.

- In Larry's letter he explains that last night it rained a lot and when it rains the moneydrops fall from the sky. Last night there was a huge storm and he lost 30 coins (or one per child). He asks the children to help him find the coins. Before the lesson begins hide 30 large laminated coins around the outside area. The children must each find a coin and can only return it to the gold pot if they can recognise the coin.

Focus of Learning
To begin to recognise coins

- Play 'Pass the coins'. This is based on 'Pass the Parcel'. Using one of each type of coin, the children pass the coins around the ring while singing, 'Pass the coin around the ring, around the ring, around the ring. Pass the coin around the ring. How much is it?' The children who have a coin stand up and must identify which coin it is.

- Play 'Raining Riches'. Using the IWB make a presentation that has coins which fall in on raindrops. The children must identify the coins as they fall from the sky. An extension to this could be that on each raindrop two coins fall. Ask the children if they can add the coins together.

* Play 'Leaping Leprechauns'. This is a team game. Make two large rainbows with amounts written on each section of the rainbow. Display the rainbows at the end of the hall or classroom. Make a simple obstacle course for each team to complete. Place two identical sets of laminated gold coins in a gold pot. The first player from each team picks out a coin, crosses the obstacle course and places the coin on the correct value on the rainbow. The next player does the same. The winning team is the first to complete their rainbow.

Art and Display Ideas

* Paint and collage a large rainbow and a leprechaun for display.
* Using lots of coins, ask the children to create their own simple picture. Photograph and use for the display.
* Using tissue paper and glue create a rainbow-style picture.
* Using small squares of coloured paper cut out of magazines and wrapping paper, make a collaged rainbow. Use this as a background for mounting the children's coins.
* Make a money tree. Paint a tree and use notes as the leaves and use the coins to create a fruit effect on the tree.

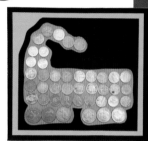

Practical Activities

* Play 'Rainbow Riches'. Make a set of laminated boards with lots of raindrops with coins on. Make cards with coins on, a leprechaun card and a pot of gold card. The children take it in turns to pick a card out of a green leprechaun hat. If they pick a coin card they should cover the corresponding coin on their board with an actual coin. If they pick a leprechaun card they must put all their coins back. If they pick a pot of gold card they can place an extra coin on their board. The winner is the child who covers all their coins first.

* Play 'Give the Gold'. Give each child a leprechaun hat and a bag of gold. In the bag of gold place a 1p, 2p, 5p, 10p, 20p, 50p, £1 and £2. Make a spinner with these amounts on and place a gold pot in the middle of the room. The children take it in turns to spin the spinner and whichever coin they land on they remove it from their bag of gold and place it in the gold pot. The winner of the game is the first child to get rid of all their coins.

Cross-curricular Links

* **Science** – Learn about the weather and rainbows. What makes a rainbow? What are the colours in a rainbow? Learn the rainbow song to help learn the colours.
* **Literacy** – Learn about the origin of leprechauns. Read lots of stories that include a leprechaun and other such magical characters, for example, *Irish Leprechaun Stories* by Bairbre McCarthy (Mercier Press, 1998) or *The Story of the Leprechaun* by Katherine Tegen and Sally Anne Lambert (HarperCollins, 2011).
* **French** – Learn the colours of the rainbow in French. Play 'Fruit Salad' using the colours of the rainbow. When you say, 'Rainbow,' the children all swap places.

The Shape Kingdom

Whole-class Starter

- Enter the class as the Queen of Shape. You are very upset because all the shapes in the kingdom have been eaten by the Shape Monster and the only shapes left are the royal shapes. Show the children the royal shapes (large 2D gold shapes) and ask them if they can identify the shapes.
- The Queen of Shape revises the shapes the children may know and extends them to learn some new shapes by playing 'Splat the Shape'. Using an IWB or a large board display the shapes and the children can take it in turns to come out and splat a shape (with a fly swatter) and identify the shape. Reverse the game so that the queen then asks the children to splat the shape she names. This game can also be played as a team game with two or three teams. The first team to splat the correct shape wins a point.
- The queen explains that the Shape Monster has eaten EVERYTHING in the Shape Kingdom. He has eaten the castle, the trees, the royal carriage and even the royal army. She asks the children if they can help her rebuild the kingdom and protect the shapes. She says that the kingdom and her

Focus of Learning
To learn how to recognise 2D shapes

army were made out of all the shapes the children have been talking about. Do they think they can rebuild them? The queen shows the children her special shape board which she uses to design her kingdom. She demonstrates how to make a tree by moving a rectangle and some circles. She also demonstrates how to enlarge and rotate the shapes. The queen then invites the children to have a go at creating things for her kingdom while constantly talking about the shapes and their properties.

Practical Activities

- Play 'Shape Builders'. Prepare a large selection of laminated shapes. Ask the children to use the shapes to build a new Shape Kingdom.
- Play 'Beware the Monster'. Make a set of laminated shape

around the hall and on a given signal they must choose a mat or shape to sit by or on. You pick a clue or name of a shape out of the box. If it corresponds with a child's shape then that child is out of the game. The winner is the child who remains in the game the longest.

Art and Display Ideas

- Using paper and glue help the children to cut out lots of shapes to create a soldier for the queen's shape army.

- As a class, create an enormous Shape Kingdom on the wall. The children cut out and stick the shapes to create the Shape Kingdom using their design ideas from the Practical Activity 'Shape Builders'.
- Using the work of Paul Klee as a stimulus, create a picture of the Queen of Shape, the Shape Monster or the Shape Kingdom. Use chalk pastels to add colour.

Cross-curricular Links

- **ICT** – Ask the children to create a shape picture by dragging, enlarging, rotating and colouring shapes using a computer.
- **Literacy** – Use the book *Bear in a Square* by Stella Blackstone and Debbie Harter (Barefoot Books, 2006). Read with the children and spot and discuss the shapes on every page.
- **Literacy** – Create a story about the Shape Kingdom and act it out using puppets and a puppet theatre.

boards and a set of corresponding shape words or picture cards. Place the cards in a feely-box along with several cards showing a picture of the Shape Monster. The children take it in turns to pick a card out of the box. If they pick a shape word or picture they place it on the correct place on their board. If they pick out the Shape Monster they must remove one card from their board. The winner is the child who covers all the squares on their board first.

- Play 'Shape Pictures'. Give each child in the group a picture made out of shapes. The children spin a spinner with corresponding shapes on, or the names of the shapes. They must colour in the appropriate shape on their picture, depending on where the spinner stops.

- Play 'Shape Run Around'. This game should be played in the hall or playground. Place a large picture of each shape on a mat or wall area. Make a set of cards with shape clues (properties) or shape names on and place them in a feely-box or bag. The children move

Mr Odd and Mrs Even

Whole-class Starter

- Enter the classroom as Mrs Even. You are moaning about your husband Mr Odd. Pull lots of socks from your washing basket (these could be real socks or laminated pictures) and explain to the children that they can tell your socks because they are always in pairs, but Mr Odd always has odd socks. Hold up one sock and explain to the children that this sock has not got a pair, therefore it is odd. Then hold up two socks that are the same and explain that they are your socks because they are a pair. Then hold up three blue socks and say, 'Look – I have a pair but I also have an odd one'. Continue to talk to the children holding up different amounts of socks. Explain that if they can put the socks into pairs they belong to you but if there is an odd sock it belongs to Mr Odd. Invite the children to help sort the washing basket out into piles of Mr Odd's washing and piles of Mrs Even's washing. Produce a washing line and place the socks on the line in groups. For example, one red sock, two green socks, three blue socks, four pink

Focus of Learning
To learn about odd and even numbers

socks. Then ask the children to help you label the socks as odd or even.

- Mrs Even empties her washing basket to reveal lots of numbers. She challenges the children to find out which numbers are her favourites and which are Mr Odd's favourites. She picks up a number and asks the children to try to work out if it is an odd or even number. She encourages them to use the washing line to help. She pins the number on the correct place on the washing line.

- Play 'Whose Washing?'. Mrs Even empties her bag of washing (lots of clothes with numbers on). Make sure that there is an item of clothing for each child. She has two washing baskets, one that has the word 'odd' written on it and one that has 'even' written on it. She gives each child an item of clothing and asks them to place their item in the correct washing basket.

a spinner or a dice that has the words 'odd' and 'even' on and also a raindrop. The children will need a whiteboard pen. If they roll or spin the word 'odd' or the word 'even' they write a number of their choice on a piece of washing. If they roll a raindrop they must rub one number out.

- Play 'Mr Odd and Mrs Even'. Make each child in the group a board with a picture of Mr Odd and Mrs Even on and the words 'odd' and 'even'. The children take it in turns to pick out a number from a bag and put it on the correct picture.

Art and Display Ideas

- Paint and collage a large Mr Odd and Mrs Even.
- Paint and collage large socks, some as pairs and some individual socks.
- Paint large items of clothing.
- Create numbers in the style of Jasper Johns and arrange them around the corresponding character on the display.

Cross-curricular Links

- **Literacy** – Read and enjoy the story of *Mrs Mopple's Washing Line* by Anita Hewitt and Robert Broomfield (Red Fox, 1994).
- **History** – Discuss with the children how people used to wash their clothes. Show the children artefacts from the past that relate to washing such as a mangle, dolly peg, clothes horse and washboard.
- **PSHCE** – Discuss with the children other ways of keeping clean. We wash our clothes but what else must we do to keep clean? Talk about the importance of being clean and what happens if we do not wash ourselves and our clothes.

Practical Activities

- Play 'Leg it to the Line'. Divide the children into two teams and put up two washing lines, one for each team. Place a giant washing basket in the middle of the room full of clothes with numbers on. Make a dice that has the word 'odd' on two sides, 'even' on two sides and pictures of raindrops on two sides. Each team member takes it in turn to throw the dice. If it lands on the word 'even' they must race to the washing basket, collect an item of clothing that has an even number attached to it and hang it on their washing line. If they roll the word 'odd' they must collect an item of clothing with an odd number attached to it and hang it on the washing line. If they roll a raindrop they must remove an item from the line. The team with the most washing on the line at the end of the game is the winner.
- Play 'Wacky Washing'. Make each child in the group a laminated board with a washing line with clothes on it. Make

Broken Broomsticks

Whole-class Starter

- Enter the classroom as Wanda the Witch carrying a bag of laminated broomsticks, all of different lengths, one of which is broken. You are upset because your broomstick is broken and you cannot work out which of your spare broomsticks to use. Put your broken broomstick on the board and one by one get the other broomsticks out and compare them. Ask the children if they can help you figure out which broomstick is the right one to use. As the children make suggestions, focus in on the appropriate language 'too long', 'too short' and 'the same as'. Find a broomstick that is the same length as the broken one and thank the children for their help.

- Wanda notices that the children have been using phrases like 'too long' and 'too short'. She explains to the children that these are words we use when we are measuring. She asks the children to help her order all her broomsticks from the shortest to the longest. She plays a game with the children by asking them to close their eyes. She swaps two broomsticks over and asks the children which ones have moved and to put them into the correct order again.

- Play 'Broom Broom.' Using the IWB, prepare a presentation in which three different-coloured broomsticks fly in. Give each child three paddles or fans. Each paddle or fan is the same colour as one of the broomsticks. The children must guess which broomstick is the longest or the shortest and hold up the appropriate colour.

Focus of Learning
To understand the concept of 'longer than' and 'shorter than' and to compare a selection of objects according to length

In the presentation another three broomsticks fly in. Ask the children to identify the longest and shortest broomsticks.

Practical Activities

- Play 'Lacey Lengths'. Give each child a lace sweet. The children take it in turns to roll a dice and whatever number it lands on they must take that number of bites from their lace. After each turn discuss who has the longest, who has the shortest and whose laces are the same length. (Check for any known food allergies before foodstuffs are used in classroom activities.)
- Play 'A Bag Full of Broomsticks'. Make a selection of laminated brooms – all different lengths. Put the broomsticks in a bag. Each child takes it in turn to pick a broomstick out of the bag. Then they should put the broomsticks in order, according to length. Discuss the terms 'longest', 'shortest' and 'same'.
- Play 'On Your Broomstick'. Make a selection of larger broomsticks and give each child in the group a broom. Make a dice spinner that has 'same', 'longer' and 'shorter' on the different sides. The children in the group walk around the school with their broomsticks and at different areas of the school the teacher rolls the dice. The children must find objects in that area which are longer than, shorter than or the same as their broomsticks, according to what the dice lands on.

Art and Display Ideas

- Paint and collage a large witch for display.
- Paint a selection of broomsticks. Encourage the children to mix their own brown paint to develop the skill of colour mixing. Use these broomsticks for the title and display of the witch collage.
- Make scary witch hands. The children draw around their own hand but not the top of the fingers. Using a pencil the children should extend the top of the fingers to create scary witch fingers. Then use green paint to create a 'witchy' look.

- Using charcoal create a circular picture of a witch on a broomstick.
- Make a witch object picture. Using oil or chalk pastels ask the children to create spiderwebs on their paper, then paint and collage a black object that would belong to a witch onto the background. For example a hat, cat, cauldron, broomstick or bat.

Cross-curricular Links

- **D&T** – Using twigs and sticks make broomsticks. Decorate them with recyclable materials.
- **Art** – Using inspiration from the series of paintings called *The Scream* (1983–1910) by Edvard Munch, use a variety of paint techniques to create a picture. For example, use thick ready-mixed paint and simple tools such as toothbrushes, combs and sticks to create different effects.

Day and Night

Whole-class Starter

- Read and enjoy *Big Bear Little Bear* by David Bedford and Jane Chapman (Little Tiger Press, 2006). Discuss with the children why they think Little Bear is worried about night-time. Discuss the characteristics of night and day.
- Give the children pictures of things that can only be seen in the day, and pictures of things that can only be seen at night. Put two circles in the middle of the floor, one called 'day' and one called 'night'. Ask the children to decide where the pictures should be placed. Discuss any incorrect decisions.

Focus of Learning
To understand the terms 'night' and 'day' and their characteristics

- On the IWB display vocabulary that is related to night and day for example 'morning', 'evening', 'dark', 'light', 'sun', 'moon', 'dusk', 'dawn', 'midday', 'midnight'. Drag the words to make lists that display day words and night words.
- Give each child a paddle with a picture of the Moon and the word 'night' on one side and a

picture of the Sun and the word 'day' on the other. Using the IWB create a presentation in which a picture or word flashes up. The children must decide if the word relates to day or night and they must show the appropriate side of the paddle. Discuss their choices.

Practical Activities

- Make lots of boards with pictures of things that you find in the day and at night – all the boards should be slightly different. Make a dice or spinner which has the words 'day' and 'night' on it as well as a picture of Little Bear. Each child takes it in turn to spin the spinner or roll the dice. If it lands on the word 'day' the child must cover the appropriate images, and do the same if it lands on 'night'. If the dice or spinner lands on Little Bear the children must uncover all the images.

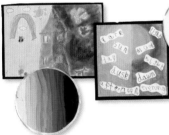

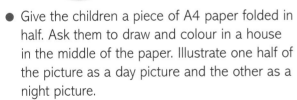

- Give the children a piece of A4 paper folded in half. Ask them to draw and colour in a house in the middle of the paper. Illustrate one half of the picture as a day picture and the other as a night picture.
- Discuss with the children what they do at

specific times of the day, for example morning, afternoon, evening and night. Ask the children to illustrate their thoughts by drawing a picture to represent each different time in the day.

Art and Display Ideas

- Colour-mix circles of blue from dark to light and light to dark.
- Draw and chalk-pastel large pictures that represent day and night.
- Using chalk pastels create a picture of two halves with one half using daytime colours and the other half using night-time colours. Ask the children to write words that represent day and night in the appropriate half.

Cross-curricular Links

- **Art** – Using the artist Van Gogh as a stimulus, ask the children to use collage materials to recreate his famous painting *Starry Night* (1889).
- **PSHCE** – Discuss with the children the importance of sleep. Ask the children what time they go to bed and why it is important to have lots of sleep.
- **Science** – Investigate facts about the Sun and the Moon. Discuss with the children why we need day and night.

23

Dino Doubles

Whole-class Starter

- Enter the classroom as Ug the Caveman. Explain to the children that strange things are happening in the Land of the Dinosaurs. Instead of them becoming extinct they are doubling. Ask the children if they know what that means. Take some pictures of dinosaurs out of the sack you have brought with you and put them on the board while you explain. For example, you would say, 'There used to be one stegosaurus and then the stegosaurus doubled and now there are two! There used to be two diplodocuses and then they doubled and now there are four. Can you see?' Repeat and then ask the children to explain what they think doubling means.
- Ug decides to use the IWB to see if the children understand doubling. He gives

Focus of Learning
To understand doubling as repeated addition

each child a piece of cave rock to write on and a piece of chalk, (a whiteboard and a pen). He puts pictures of different types of dinosaur on the board and asks the children if they can double them and write the answers on their boards. He shows how to double and how to write doubling as a repeated addition.

- Play 'Dealing Dino Doubles'. Make a set of dinosaur doubling cards. Each pair should illustrate a dino double, for example, if one card has four Tyrannosaurus Rex

Create and Display: Mathematics

dinosaurs, its corresponding pair should have eight Tyrannosaurus Rex dinosaurs. Make enough pairs so that you can deal out a single card to each child. Play some relevant music, for example the *Jurassic Park* title track, and while the music is playing the children must move around and find their pair. The children should then take it turns to read out their sum, for example, 'Double 2 is 4.'

Practical Activities

- Play 'Double Dinosaurs'. Make a large board game for a group to play. The children must roll a dice and work their way from start to finish following the dinosaur footprints. If they land on a space on which there are dinosaurs they must double the number of dinosaurs and collect that many from a basket of mini dinosaurs. If they land on a caveman, the caveman will capture all the dinosaurs from their pile! At the end of the game the child with the most dinosaurs is the winner.

- Play 'Discover the Dinosaurs'. In a small group take the children on a hunt for dinosaurs around the school. Make sure that in advance you have placed groups of dinosaurs (either toys or pictures) around the school. When the children discover some dinosaurs they must double the number and write the answer on a whiteboard.
- Play 'Cross the Jungle'. Make some giant dinosaur footprints. On one side should be a number and on the other side its corresponding double. Challenge the children to cross the jungle. To do this, one child at a time should stand on a footprint, read the number and double it. They can turn the footprint over to see if they are right. If they are right, they move on one, if they are wrong they must go to the back of the line. Each time you should change the order of the footprints.

Art and Display Ideas

- Paint and collage a large dinosaur.
- Paint and collage individual dinosaurs.
- Make dinosaur footprints from large pieces of paper.
- Cut out bones from white paper and stick them onto a black background to make a dinosaur skeleton picture.
- Use textured wallpaper or sandpaper and charcoal to practise cave painting.

Cross-curricular Links

- **Small World Play** – Play with a dinosaur and caveman set.

- **Literacy** – Read and enjoy a selection of dinosaur stories (for example, *Dinosaurs Galore!* by Giles Andreae and David Wojtowycz [Orchard, 2005], *Bumpus Jumpus Dinosaurumpus* by Tony Mitton and Guy Parker-Rees [Orchard, 2003], *Harry and the Bucketful of Dinosaurs* by Ian Whybrow and Adrian Reynolds [Puffin, 2009]) and make a class dinosaur fact book.

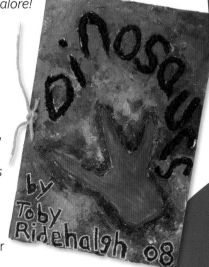

- **D&T** – Make a moving dinosaur using recyclable materials and pneumatics to make it move.

Positional People

Whole-class Starter

- On the IWB display a picture of a tree. Explain to the children that it might look like an ordinary tree but in fact it is a very special tree because people live inside! However, they are not normal people, they are called the Positional People, because they live in the tree in different positions. Click on the IWB presentation so that a family appears at the top of the tree. Explain that the Top family lives at the top of the tree. Click again so that Mr Under appears upside down under one of the branches. Explain that he lives under his branch and he even walks under the branches in his special shoes with suckers on so he can hold on upside down. Click again so that another house and family appears next to Mr Under. Explain that this is the Next To family. Repeat telling stories of the different inhabitants of the tree, such as Mr and Mrs In Between, the Left family, the Right family, Mr and Mrs Above,

Focus of Learning
To learn to use everyday words to describe position

the Inside family.
- Play 'Who's Who'. Prepare laminated boards of the finished tree picture and give one to each pair. Pull out of a bag a positional word, for example, 'in between'. The children work in pairs to discuss which family that is by thinking about what the word means. They then circle the correct family on their board.
- Play 'Positional People'. Take the children into a large space, for example the hall or playground. Ask the children to work in groups of three. Give each group a card with a positional word on. The children must think of a way to create that position using their bodies for the other children to guess. Ask one group at a time to perform their position.

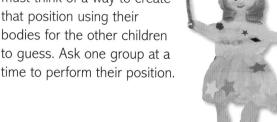

Practical Activities

- Play 'Peeping Positions'. This game is based on the idea of 'Kim's Game' from the novel *Kim* by Rudyard Kipling. Place a selection of objects on a tray. The objects must be positioned in such a way that they display the positions that have been discussed previously. The teacher asks the children to identify objects that are in different positions. For example, *Which object is next to…, under the…, in between the…*

- Play 'I Spy the Positional People'. Using the board from the carpet session, give each child a board and whiteboard pen. Make a spinner with different positions on and include a blank tree on one section of the spinner. The children take it in turns to spin and whatever position they land on they circle the appropriate family. If they land on the blank tree they must rub out all their circled families and start again.

Art and Display Ideas

- Investigate the work of LS Lowry. Using the picture *The Cripples* (1949) as a stimulus look at Lowry's portrayal of people. Discuss their different positions within the picture. Ask the children to create their own Lowry-style artwork using charcoal or watercolour pencils.

Encourage them to think about where they position the different people.

- Ask the children to paint and collage the different families on the Positional Tree.
- Create a tree hand print collage. The children draw around their hands using paint and collage materials they turn their hands into trees.
- Draw around a leaf and turn it into a tree and use watercolours to paint it. Four trees could be created and painted with seasonal colours.
- Using the children in the class, place them in different positions to spell out the title 'POSITIONAL PEOPLE'. Photograph and use for the display title.

- Ask the children to paint a tree with a background colour that reflects the seasons. For example, autumn – red, gold, yellow, orange; spring – green, yellow, pink and so on.

Cross-curricular Links

- **Science** – Learn about the seasons of the year and relate them to how the trees change in each of the seasons. Using sponge techniques and watercolour paints ask the children to create four trees that represent the seasons.
- **Art** – Using the work of Andy Goldsworthy as inspiration, encourage the children to use the trees in the environment and reproduce a collage hanging frieze based on his work.
- **Environmental Science** – Identify the trees in the school grounds or a nearby park. Look at different trees and establish their leaves, fruits and names. As a group pick a tree and create a poster identifying the features of their chosen tree.

Hundred Square Hippy

Focus of Learning
To learn to count, recognise and write numerals to 100

Whole-class Starter

- Enter the class as the Hundred Square Hippy. Explain to the children that you love numbers and you can't pick your favourite number so you have made a special square that includes all the numbers from 1 to 100. Show the children a giant hundred square on the IWB. Reveal that you have special hundred squares that are mini size that you give to children who are 'cool, man' and work hard at learning their numbers to 100. You will need to pre-make tiny laminated hundred square badges to give out as rewards for excellent knowledge.

- The Hundred Square Hippy explains to the children that he is going to teach them all about his hundred square and he begins to explain how it all works. He explains that the hundred square is made up of rows and columns and explains how they work. For example, he points out the tens column and shows how the rows begin with the same number and so on. Using the IWB the Hundred Square Hippy tests the children's knowledge by pointing to different numbers and asking the children to call them out. He then asks different children to come out, pick a number and reveal what number it is.

- Play 'Discover the Digits'. The Hundred Square Hippy covers up lots of numbers on his hundred square. Give each child a whiteboard and pen and ask them to write down the numbers that are hidden. The hippy reveals the numbers and the children check their answers. This could be extended by showing only a part of the hundred square with the number missing. Once again the children write the answer on their whiteboard and the hippy reveals the number. Discuss with the children ways of discovering the correct number by using their knowledge of the hundred squares rows and columns

Practical Activities

- Play 'Flower Power'. Make a set of laminated flowers with a hundred square in the middle and separate numbers on the petals. The hundred square in the middle has gaps that correspond with the numbers on the petals. The object of the game is for the children to draw a line from the number on the petal to the appropriate number on the square.

- Play 'Hundred Square Bingo'. Give each child a hundred square with 15 numbers blanked out (make each board different). Using a bingo machine call out the number and the children must fill in the appropriate numbers. The first child to fill in all their numbers wins the game and shouts, 'Hippy House.' Alternatively – give each child a hundred square with only 15 numbers written on. The first child to tick off all their numbers wins the game and shouts, 'Hippy House.'
- Play 'Dudes, Dash to the Digits'. Make a giant hundred square and lots of small laminated flower discs that have numbers between 1 and 100 on the back. The flower discs must fit over one square. Set up a simple obstacle course that leads to the hundred square. Split the group into two teams and give each team ten flower discs. The object of the game is for each team to get rid of their ten discs. To do this, a member of each team tackles the obstacle course to get to the hundred square with a disc and place it on the correct number. The team to finish first, having placed all their discs correctly, wins.

Art and Display Ideas

- Paint and collage a large hippy and a large hundred square on a giant flower.
- Using inspiration from the artist Romero Britto create a picture using oil pastels.
- Using materials and wool recreate a flower power picture.
- Create words related to the hundred square in 1960s style and use them on the display.
- Make a clay flower tile each. Join the tiles together to create a giant class montage.
- For a class art project each child could tie-dye a square piece of fabric and print a symbol that represents the 1960s onto the fabric. Sew all the squares together to make a class wall hanging.

Cross-curricular Links

- **History** – Learn about life in the 1960s. Create a fact book about the 1960s.
- **Science** – Have a class competition to see who can grow the healthiest plant. All the children should design and paint their own terracotta pot in a 1960s style.

Pick a Pig, Build a Bond

Whole-class Starter

- Explain to the children that today you have a special visitor who is going to help the class with their maths. Today they are going to be learning about how to make 10. Tell them that the third little piggy from the Three Little Pigs' story is going to help them. Explain that he is the cleverest of the pigs because he built his house out of bricks and he is also really good at making 10 because he needs ten bricks to build the walls of his house. Introduce the children to your pig puppet. Mr Pig starts by checking if the children can count to 10 forwards and backwards. He checks that they can count on from a given number to 10. For example, start from 3 and count to 10.
- Using either play bricks (DUPLO™) or a prepared *PowerPoint*® presentation Mr Pig introduces the children to the numbers that make 10. Several bricks bounce onto the screen and together the children count

Focus of Learning
To learn to recall number bonds that make 10

the bricks and then, with the help of Mr Pig, they work out how many bricks they need to make 10. The missing bricks bounce in and together they count the ten bricks to check they are correct. Repeat this several times. Mr Pig asks the children what they would do if they had no bricks. Could they work the number bonds out using anything else or just their brains? He shows them a number on the board and asks them if they can make ten. He encourages the children to either use their fingers or count on in their head. This activity can be repeated several times.

He introduces them to his favourite game 'Run Piggy Run'. Make a set of ten large houses with numbers 0 to 10 written on and a set of 30 laminated pigs that correspond to the houses to make the number 10. In a large space place the houses around the wall and place the pig cards in the middle. Give one child a wolf mask and on saying the words 'I'll huff and I'll puff' the other children must pick a pig card and run to the correct house that would make 10. For example, if a child has a pig with the number 4 on they need to run to a house that has number 6 on. The last child to find their house becomes the wolf or is out of the game. At the end of each game, check the children's choices and correct any misconceptions.

Practical Activities

● Play 'Pick a Pig, Make a Bond'. Make a set of laminated boards with houses on that have numbers 0 to 10 written on their front doors.

Make lots of piggy cards with corresponding numbers 0 to 10 on their bellies. Also include a wolf card. Place the pig cards and the wolf card in a bag or feely-box. Give each child a board. The object of the game is to match a pig to a house so that their two numbers added together make 10. If they pick the wolf card out, they must remove all their pigs and start again. The winner is the child who covers all their houses correctly.

● Play 'Tower of Ten'. Make a set of laminated brick cards with numbers 0 to 10 written on and several wolf cards. Either place a small basket of bricks in the middle of the table or use large bricks in the hall or carpet area. Place the cards in a bag or basket. Each child must pick out a brick card and work out what they need to add to the number on the brick to make 10. If correct, they collect a brick from the basket and have another go. They keep going until they make a mistake or they pick out a wolf card. If they pick out a wolf card their tower gets blown down and they must start again. The winner is the child who builds a tower to 10 or the highest tower.

● Play 'Time for Ten'. Make a set of laminated number searches filled with numbers 0 to 10. Give each child a whiteboard and a pen. Using a 30-second timer, the children must find and circle as many bonds that make 10 as possible within the time.

Art and Display Ideas

● Ask the children to work in small groups to create the three houses made out of straw, sticks and bricks for display.

● Make a personalised pig. Ask the children to draw a large pig and personalise it with things that represent them. Use watercolours to add colour.

● Scrunch sheets of A4 paper and then flatten them out to give a crinkled effect. Draw a pig picture and use wax crayons to colour.

● Colour-mix shades of pink and paint the piece of paper in stripes. Draw pig pictures. Cut out and stick onto the stripy piece of paper.

● Create a pig picture using layers of scrunched up tissue-paper.

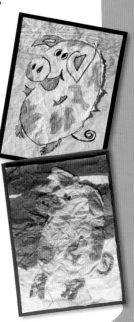

Cross-curricular Links

● **Maths** – Make a pig picture using different shapes. Use circles, triangles, squares and oval shapes.

● **ICT** – Using a paint package draw and colour in a pig. Copy and paste the pig and rotate the colours to create a picture in the style of Andy Warhol.

Take Away Teddies

Whole-class Starter

- Read and enjoy the story of *The Teddy Robber* by Ian Beck (Picture Corgi, 2006). Explain to the children that the giant in the story keeps taking away teddies from the children. Although in the story he is being naughty by 'taking away' the teddies because he upsets the children, 'taking away' numbers is actually very clever and really useful. Explain to the children how to take away numbers by using real teddies. Place some real teddies on a table and choose a child to be the 'teddy robber'. Give the 'teddy robber' a swag bag and a burglar mask to wear. Say a sum out loud, for example, 'Five teddies take away three teddies.' Put five teddies on a table and the teddy robber takes away three by putting them in his swag bag. How many are left? Repeat several times choosing different children to be the teddy robber.

Focus of Learning
To understand subtraction as 'taking away'

- Introduce the children to the minus sign. Put on the IWB a sum, for example '3 – 2 =' and all read it together. Prepare your IWB presentation so that three teddies then appear underneath the sum. Ask the children if we take away two, how many will be left? Ask children to work it out and then show it visually by making two teddies disappear and showing that there is one left. Repeat using

different sums. Finally just the written sum should appear and you should show the children how to work it out using their fingers to help them. Repeat several times.

- Play 'Take Away Teddies'. Sit the children in a circle. In a hoop in the middle of the circle, place lots of teddy-shaped cards with take away sums on that all equal the numbers 1 to 6. Around the edge of the room, place giant teddies with numbers 1 to 6 on. Play some teddy bear music. While the music is playing, children come and choose a card, read the sum and work out the answer and run to the correct answer around the room. You can quickly assess who has got the correct answer and deal with any misconceptions.

Practical Activities

- Play 'Robbing Roulette'. Make a spinner with the minus sign, the numbers 1 to 6 and a picture of the little boy from the story

on it. Give each child a swag bag and 20 teddies. The children take it in turns to spin the spinner. If it says '–4' they have to take away four teddies and give them to the teddy robber (teacher or adult wearing a mask). If it lands on the little boy, they are safe for that go. The child with the most teddies left at the end of the game is the winner.

- Make a set of teddy bear cards with minus

sums on. All the cards should have different sums. Ask the children to work out the answers using their fingers or teddy bears to help them. They should fill in the answers using a whiteboard pen.

- Play 'Teddy Bear Robber'. Make a set of cards with minus sums on and a few cards with a giant's hand on. You will also need lots of teddies. Split the group into two teams and place the teddies in the middle. Each team takes it in turn to pick a card with a minus sum on it. They work out the answer to the sum and then take that number of teddies for their team. The team with the most teddies at the end is the winning team. However, if they turn over a card with the giant's hand on, the giant takes away all their teddies!

Art and Display Ideas

- Create and build a bear using paint and collage materials.
- Paint a teddy experimenting with different brushes and strokes to create the texture of fur.
- Paint and collage the large giant or boy from the story.
- Sketch a teddy bear using pencils.
- Make a teddy bear using patchwork.
- Make some bunting with teddy bears on it.

Cross-curricular Links

- **PSHCE** – Discuss the moral issue in the story about stealing. Was it right or wrong? Why did the giant take away the little boy's teddy?
- **PSHCE** – Ask the children to bring their favourite teddy into school and hold a teddy bears' picnic.
- **D&T** – Sew a beanie teddy bear.

Multiplication Martians

Whole-class Starter

- The class receives a video link from outer space (a DVD of the teacher as a Martian). The Martian explains that he is from the planet Mars and on his planet the Martians are called Multiplication Martians because they have special powers that mean they can multiply very easily. He explains that because the children are merely earthlings he knows they do not know how to multiply but he can show them how to do it. The Martian shows the children that Martians have special body parts in order to make it easy. For example, he shows them he has two antennae, three eyes, six arms, five toes, etc. He uses pictures of Martians with two antennae to visually demonstrate the two times table. He encourages the children to join in and chant the times table. This could be extended to look at other times tables by focusing on the different body parts of the Martians.

Focus of Learning
To understand the language of multiplication and how to multiply two numbers

- The Martian explains that on his planet they speak a special language. He shows the children the multiplication language. For example, 'lots of', 'groups of', 'multiplied by', 'multiply' and 'times'. He also shows them his special planet sign which means the same as these words. He shows the multiplication sign. He invites the children to play 'I Spy Multiply'. Make an IWB presentation with words and symbols, some of which are from the multiplication planet and others that are not. The children must watch carefully and if they

see a multiplication word they must make a multiplication sign by crossing their arms in front of them and shout the relevant word.

- In a large space play 'Multiplication Mix-up'. Ask the children to move around the hall and on a given signal they must get into groups according to the number you have said. You then pose a multiplication problem to the groups by asking them to find the number of eyes or noses or fingers in the group and write the multiplication sum on a whiteboard.

Practical Activities

- Play 'Multiplication Martians'. Make a board with planets on. Add a large selection of mini Martians with multiplication sums on. The children take it in turns to pick out a Martian and they must work out the sum. If they are correct they place the Martian on a planet. You should also include several spaceships and if they pick out a spaceship they must remove all their Martians. The object is to cover all the planets with Martians.
- Play 'Martian Madness'. Make a set of large Martian heads with multiplication sums on. Place them around the school or a large area. The children must hunt for the Martians and on discovering one work out the multiplication sum and record the answer on an answer card.

- Play 'Space Odyssey'. Make a selection of multiplication cards and a selection of large planets

with the appropriate answers. Place the answer cards around a large space or hall. Organise the children into teams and give each team a Spacehopper™. Ask both teams a multiplication sum and a child from each team has to bounce to the correct answer. The first team to reach the answer gets a point. The team with the most points is the winner.

Art and Display Ideas

- Paint and collage a giant alien for display.
- Paint and collage individual martians for display with different numbers of body parts.
- Create some space art using celestial images for inspiration.
- Use a black background and chalk pastels. Draw the planets and create a space odyssey picture.
- Recreate the Northern Lights using wet calico and ink.

Cross-curricular Links

- **Science** – Discuss the order of the planets and encourage the children to create their own mnemonic to help them remember. For example, *My Very Easy Method Just Speeds Up Naming Planets!* (Mercury, Venus, Earth, Mars, Jupiter, Saturn, Uranus, Neptune, Planets!).
- **D&T** – Design and make a giant alien or a spaceship from recyclable materials.
- **PSHCE** – Look at ways to protect our planet. Make a poster showing ways of saving the Earth. Read and discuss *Noah and the Space Ark* by Laura Cecil and Emma Chichester Clark (Picture Puffin, 1998).

Pizza Pieces

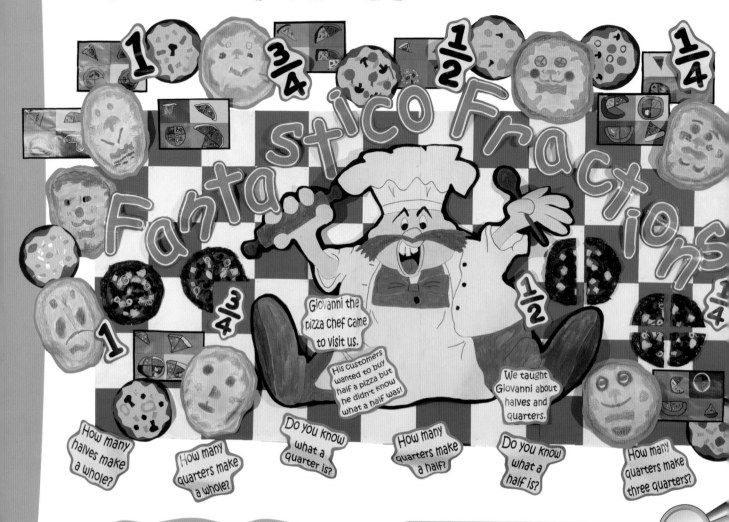

Whole-class Starter

- Enter the classroom as Giovanni the chef who has a slight problem because you only sell whole pizzas, but people are starting to order half a pizza. You do not know what to do and you thought you would ask for the children's help. Give each pair of children a paper pizza and ask them to show you what they think the customer means by half a pizza. Discuss and deal with any misconceptions. Demonstrate how to make half a pizza and reveal to the children that this is wonderful because two halves make a whole and write the fraction on the board, discussing what each numeral means, for example, 'I had one whole pizza and cut it into two pieces to make a half!'

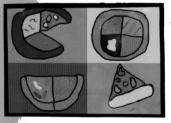

Focus of Learning
To begin to understand simple fractions, eg ¼, ½, ¾

- However, Giovanni goes on to say that his problem is even worse than this because the little *bambinos* that come in to the restaurant say they only want a quarter of a pizza. What does this mean? He asks the children to demonstrate what they think this means by using another paper pizza. Again discuss and deal with any misconceptions. Giovanni uses his real pizza and cuts it into quarters. He draws the children's attention to the fact that two quarters make a half and two halves make a whole. Write fractions on the board and discuss what the numerals mean in each one. Depending on the ability of your class, this could be extended to teach three quarters or equivalent fractions.

- Give each child a laminated pizza shape and a pen. On the IWB prepare in advance some pizza pictures depicting different fractions. The children must look at each picture and write down the fraction depicted, for example, if a whole pizza appears on the IWB, they would write '1', if half a pizza appears they would write ½. They might also write ²/₄, which you should discuss.

Practical Activities

- Play 'Pizza Pairs'. Make a set of card pairs which have pictures of pizzas as fractions on one card and on the other the written fraction. Children take it in turns to turn over two cards. If they match they may keep the pair. At the end, the child with the most cards is the winner.
- Set up a role-play 'Pizza Restaurant' with roles for a chef, a waiter and waitress and some customers. The customers should be given menus written in fractions to read. They would give their order to the waiter or waitress who writes it down using written fractions. This then gets taken to the chef who cuts the pizzas into the appropriate fractions to serve.
- Play 'Pick a Pizza'. Make laminated boards with pictures of pizzas shaded or cut into fractions. Spin a spinner or dice that has the written fractions and fraction words on. Children then cover up the appropriate fraction.
- Play 'A Piece of Pizza Please'. Around the school put up large laminated written fractions and fraction words. Give each child a laminated circle and a pen. Ask them to walk around the school. When they find a fraction they must use their pen to shade in the correct fraction on their board.

Art and Display Ideas

- Draw, paint and collage your favourite pizza. Cut the pizza into slices and label according to the fraction.
- Paint and collage a large chef.
- Using Arcimboldo as a focus ask the children to create Giovanni's face using the idea of pizza and things you would find on a pizza.
- Create a piece of pizza pop art.
- Make scrap material or collage pizzas.

Cross-curricular Links

- **D&T (Food Technology)** – Design and make pizza with different toppings on fractions of the pizza. (Check for any known food allergies before foodstuffs are used in classroom activities.)
- **PSHCE** – Visit a pizza restaurant and learn how to make an authentic Italian pizza (or watch a video online).
- **Literacy** – Write instructions for making a pizza using adverbs to describe the verbs.

37

Build It!

It has 2 circular faces.

sphere

It has 6 square faces.

Can you match the 3D shapes to their properties?

cuboid

cube

We helped Bert build using 3D shapes.

cylinder

pyramid

cone

It has no corners.

It has 6 faces. 2 of them are square.

Can you identify the shapes we have used?

It has 4 triangular faces.

It has a circular base.

Whole-class Starter

- Enter the classroom as Bert the Builder. Complain that you are used to building with just one shape as you usually use bricks, but your latest job is for the Queen of Shape and she wants you to build with a whole assortment of shapes and you are a bit unsure about it! Can the children help you? Show the children the different shapes that the queen has given you. They are all 3D shapes, for example cubes, cuboids, pyramids, cylinders, spheres, cones, triangular prisms. Show one shape at a time, telling the children what it is called and discussing its features. Then

Focus of Learning
To recognise and name 3D shapes and begin to learn their features

label the shapes with large laminated words.
- Play 'Show Your Shape'. Give each child in the class a 3D shape. From his builder's bucket Bert pulls the name of a shape. The children who have that shape must stand up and show their shape. This could be extended to pulling out a feature or property of the shape.
- Play 'Shape Swap'. Again each child needs a 3D shape. Bert plays some music and the children should walk around the room holding their shape. When the music stops, each

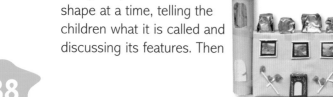

child should swap their shape with another child and also tell them the name of their shape, for example, 'It's a cone.' Again, this could be extended to telling each other a feature or property of the shape.

- Bert explains to the children that today he is also here to teach them about building 3D shapes. He gives each child a 3D shape and explains that as a class they are going to make a castle for the Queen of Shape. He begins by placing a cuboid in the middle of the carpet. He invites a child at a time to place their shape to help build the castle. After all the children have added their shapes Bert discusses with the children which shapes were good for building and which shapes were tricky. He discusses further things he could make with 3D shapes.

Practical Activities

- Play '3D Shape Lotto'. Make a lotto game matching 3D shapes to the shape names or properties.
- Play 'Build It'. Using lots of 3D blocks or construction kits ask the children to make a castle, city or town using the 3D blocks.
- Play 'The Shape Builder'. Make a set of cards with pictures of 3D shapes on. Invite the children to try to build something using the shapes they have been given.
- Play 'Spin for a Shape'. Make a spinner with pictures of the relevant 3D shapes on, for example cube, cuboid, sphere, cylinder, triangular prism, cone, pyramid. Place several blocks of each shape in the middle of the table. Each child takes it in turn to spin the spinner. Whatever shape they land on they take from the middle of the table. However,

if they spin a shape that somebody already has they must give the shape to that person. The object of the game is to collect as many shapes as possible in a given time.

- Play 'Feel for a Shape'. In pairs give each child a feely-bag or box. The first person places a shape in the bag or box and the second person must feel the shape and guess the shape by describing its properties. If they guess correctly they keep the shape.

Art and Display Ideas

- Using the 3D shapes from the lesson ask the children to build Bert the Builder and other objects for display.

- Try observational drawing of a selection of 3D shapes. Use charcoal and muted colours to create a shadow effect.
- Using images of 3D shapes, cut them out and arrange them to create a picture.

- Using cubism as an inspiration, create a giant cube and decorate each side of the cube with a symbol or picture that represents you as a person. Use felt pens to colour the symbols or pictures.

Cross-curricular Links

- **D&T** – Design and make a model using 3D shapes using a range of recyclable materials.
- **Science** – Devise a fair test to investigate whether all 3D shapes roll and discuss why.
- **Literacy** – Use word-building activities, such as blending and segmenting phonemes to read and write: c-a-t, sh-i-p, l-u-n-ch.

39

The Troll Trail

Whole-class Starter

- The class receives a letter from the troll from the story *The Three Billy Goats Gruff*) bragging that he is very clever because he eats a billy goat everyday because they can't answer his sums and cross the bridge safely. Tell the class that in order to cross the bridge they need to be able to do a complex sum bridging through 10 but that his bridge can help them. Explain to the children that the troll was right when he said that his bridge could help. Show a large bridge on the IWB with the number 10 on it. Then show the type of sums that the troll is asking the goats to complete. For example, 7 + 5. Ask the children how the bridge can help? Work with the children to work out how they can bridge through 10 to help solve the sum. For example, 7 + 3 = 10 + 2 = 12 (show this pictorially using the bridge as an empty number line with a number 10 in the middle). Reinforce to the children how knowing our number bonds to 10 makes this calculation easier.

Focus of Learning
To understand the concept of bridging through 10 when adding a single-digit number

- Play 'Trip Trap'. The children need to help the goats and in order to do this they must know their number bonds to 10 confidently. On the IWB make a trail that goes across the bridge but in order to move along the trail the children must reveal the number bonds to 10 and solve them. Give each child a number fan with numbers 0 to 10. Ask the children to hold up the correct answer before revealing it on the board.

- Explain that in order to help the goats all the children would need to answer one of the troll's tricky sums. Show the children several times how to bridge through 10 when adding a single digit. Give each child a laminated card with a picture of a bridge with the number 10 on and on the top of the card a sum. For example, 9 + 7 = ? Each child completes their sum and as a class discusses the sums.

Practical Activities

- Play 'Troll Trail'. Make a large set of bridge-shaped cards showing a troll sat under the bridge. On each of the cards wwrite a bridging sum for the children to complete. The children are sent to the first card which has the number 1 on. The children must complete the sum using the bridging method. The answer to the sum is the clue to completing the next bridging card. The children must complete the trail until they find the bridge card that does not have a troll but has the Three Billy Goats Gruff walking across safely.

- Play 'Troll Treats'. Make a set of bridging card sums. You will need lots of cards. The cards should have a bridge in the middle with the number 10 on and a sum at the top of the card. Laminate the cards. Place them face down on the carpet or table. Make a spinner that has different times on, for example 30 seconds, 1 minute, 2 minutes. and a picture of a troll and a picture of a sweet. Spin the spinner and if it lands on a time the children must compete to see how many bridging cards they can complete in that given time. The winner receives a sweet. If it lands on the sweet picture all the children in the group receive a sweet. If it lands on the troll card the children must complete every card in the middle of the table. After each go clean the cards and start again.

- Play 'Trip Trap Over the Bridge'. This game involves making a bridge using PE apparatus. Split the children into two teams and give each team a whiteboard and pen. Each team selects a troll and the troll must sit under the other team's bridge. The teacher reads out or reveals a sum on the IWB. The first child in the group must answer the sum before the troll. If the troll is first the child cannot cross the bridge but if the child answers the sum before the troll they can cross the bridge. The first team to get all their players safely over the bridge is the winner.

Art and Display Ideas

- Draw, paint and collage a huge troll for display.
- Using ripped tissue paper, wrapping paper, magazines and so on. collage a picture of the Three Billy Goats Gruff.

- Using Monet as inspiration, recreate a bridge scene using chalk pastels.
- Using pen and ink draw a picture that depicts a part of *The Three Billy Goats Gruff* story.

- Using watercolour paints on a wet piece of paper paint a bridge scene and let the colours bleed together.

Cross-curricular Links

- **PSHCE** – Using road signs as inspiration talk about staying safe on the road. Talk about the symbol for a bridge and what it means to road users. Ask the children to design a bridge to go on a road sign. Use black paper on a white or yellow background.
- **D&T** – Design and make a bridge using newspaper. The bridge must support a specific weight or object.

Mrs Measure

Whole-class Starter

- Enter the classroom as Mrs Measure with an assortment of measuring tools, for example tape measure, scales, balances, ruler, trundle wheel, measuring jug. Introduce yourself to the children and discuss the word 'measure' and what it means. Show the children the measuring tools and ask if they know what they are and what they are used for. Invite the children to play a game. Show the children pictures or items that can be measured and ask them to choose which measuring tool would be used to measure that particular item. For example, a bag of sugar would be measured using scales or balances, a hand would be measured using a ruler or tape measure.

Focus of Learning
To introduce the concept of measuring and the vocabulary and tools associated with measuring

- Mrs Measure explains to the children that all these measuring tools are very important and they all do different things and have different words that are associated with them. She asks the children if they know any of the words associated with her measuring tools. Mrs Measure chooses one of her measuring tools and discusses with the children its name, what it does and what unit it measures in. For example, she holds up a ruler and explains that this measures the length, height or width of objects in centimetres and millimetres. She repeats this with all her tools.

- Play 'Splat It!'. Prepare an IWB presentation that has words relating to different types of measuring tools, for example 'length', 'weight', 'centimetres', 'kilograms', 'metres', 'litres'. Split the class into two teams and give each team a splatter. A member from each team stands with their back to the board holding the splatter. Mrs Measure holds up a measuring tool and the children must turn around and splat a word that is associated with that measuring tool.

Practical Activities

- Play 'Miracle Measure'. Make a spinner that has pictures of different types of measuring instruments on, for example a ruler, set of scales, measuring jug. Make a set of cards with different pictures on and put them in a bag, for example a playground, table, book, water, shoe, apple, flour, door. Each child picks a picture out of the bag. They spin the spinner and try to match their object to the correct measuring instrument. Discuss with the children the best measuring options.

- Play 'Measure It'. Prepare a list of objects that you would like the children to measure. They must decide what measuring tool to use, measure the object, record the information on their sheet and discuss their answers with the rest of the group. Discuss the importance of accuracy as well as the correct choice of measuring implement.
- Play 'Guess the Measure'. Make a set of boards with pictures of different types of measuring tools on. Make a selection of picture cards of items that you could measure.

The children take it in turn to pick a card and try to guess what measuring tool you would use to measure this item. If they are correct they cover the measuring tool on their board with a card. The first person to cover all their pictures wins the game.

- Play 'Measure Me'. Mrs Measure allows the children to measure their own height and weight. She encourages the children to measure different body parts for example head, hand, finger, leg, and talks to them about the most appropriate type of measuring tool. The children record their findings.

Art and Display Ideas

- Paint and collage a large picture of Mrs Measure for display.
- Draw and paint pictures of measuring tools.
- Art Attack pictures – Using an array of measuring implements ask the children to create a picture. The children can then either sketch the picture or have it photographed.
- Invite the children to create and draw their own Measure family. They could include Mr Measure, Mrs Measure, the Measure children and the Measure pets. The children could include measurements on their drawings.

Cross-curricular Links

- **D&T (Food Technology)** – Make simple fairy cakes allowing the children to measure out the correct quantities. (Check for any known food allergies before foodstuffs are used in classroom activities.)
- **D&T (Food Technology)** – Make smoothies allowing the children to measure out the correct quantities.
- **ICT and Maths** – Encourage the children to measure one another's height and record the information using a data-handling package on the computer.

Digital and Analogue Clocks

Whole-class Starter

- Two characters enter the class and introduce themselves as Anna Logue and Digi Dude (If this is not possible you could prepare a DVD.) They are best friends and they like to do the same things but in different ways; their favourite thing is to tell the time but they do it using different clocks. They each show their type of clock and they ask the children if they can explain how they are different. Anna sets her clock to one o'clock and shows the children how it works, identifying the hour and minute hand. Digi sets his clock to one o'clock and explains that although his clock has no hands it is just the same. It has hours displayed before the two dots in the middle and minutes displayed after. To check the children know the difference, prepare a display for use on an IWB in which different clocks flash on the screen and the children must shout out if it is a digital or analogue clock.
- Play 'I Spy the Time'. Give

Focus of Learning
To begin to tell the time using digital and analogue clocks

each child a laminated square card with a blank analogue clock on one side and a blank digital clock on the other. Using the IWB show the children a time, displayed as analogue or digital, the children must write the corresponding time on the appropriate blank clock. Discuss the answer and correct any misconceptions.

- Play 'Mix and Match'. Make a set of laminated analogue and digital clocks in pairs, each pair showing the same time. Give each child a card. The object of this activity is for the children to find the corresponding time on a different style of clock. For example, one child would have the digital time 3:30 and another would have the corresponding analogue time.

Practical Activities

- Play 'Beat the Clock'. Make a set of large analogue clocks with different times on (make sure they are appropriate to the children's ability). Make a set of smaller corresponding digital clocks. Place the analogue clocks around the hall or large space. Using a stopwatch, on a given signal the children must race to place all their digital clocks next to the correct analogue clock. This game can be played in teams or individually. The object is to get the quickest time but with all the correct answers. Any mistakes incur a five-second penalty.
- Play 'Connecting Clocks'. This game is similar to Pelmanism. Make a set of laminated jigsaw cards that connect together. Make one set red and one set blue. On the blue set put analogue times and on the red set, digital times. Place all the cards facedown on the table. The children take it in turns to pick a red and blue card. If the times

correspond, they can connect the cards and keep them. If they do not, they must put the cards back, face down.
- Play 'Half and Half'. Make a set of cards that are half analogue clocks and half digital clocks (you will need lots of cards). Make a spinner that has one minute, 30 seconds, two minutes and 20 seconds written on it. Make two sections treats. The children take it in turns to spin the spinner. If it lands on the treat section

they all get a treat, such as a small sweet or raisins. If it lands on a time, for example one minute, the children must see how many half-and-half cards they can correctly complete in one minute. They keep every correctly answered card. The winner is the child who completes the most cards correctly. (Check for any known food allergies before foodstuffs are used in classroom activities.)

Art and Display Ideas

- Ask the children to create an analogue clock using different themed objects to represent the numbers, for example cutlery, umbrellas and raindrops.
- Using fluorescent paper and black card the children should cut out digital times and stick them down, displayed like a digital clock.
- Show the children a variety of different analogue clocks and ask the children to sketch the clocks.

Cross-curricular Links

- **D&T** – Using objects that have numbers on, ask the children to make an analogue clock. They can use any objects that have numbers on (for example, dice, telephone buttons, remote control keys, newspaper cuttings).
- **ICT** – Using a *Word*® package the children should work in groups of four. Each child in the group creates their own analogue clock showing a time. As a group they join the clocks together to create a digital time.

Once Upon a Number

Whole-class Starter

- The class receives a special giant book from Fairy Tale Land (prepare a giant book to use). Read the story to the children and they can discover that the fairy tales are actually mathematical word problems. Present the children with the first problem and they should discuss and solve the problem. For example, 'Jack had to climb up seven leaves on his beanstalk and then another six leaves. How many leaves did he climb altogether?' Talk to the class about which words help them solve the problem. Ask the children to work with their chatting chum to solve another word problem. Discuss the language used and how it helps them.

- Using the IWB, present the children with all the vocabulary related to addition and subtraction word problems, for example 'how many', 'altogether', 'plus', 'total', 'more than', 'take away', 'find the difference', 'less than', 'minus', 'count on' or 'count back'. Ask the children to sort the vocabulary into two groups, addition and subtraction, and display

Focus of Learning
To use the vocabulary relating to addition and subtraction to solve and create word problems

them on the board underneath the correct mathematical symbol. Give each child a card and sit the children in a circle. Place two hoops in the middle of the floor with the addition sign in one and the subtraction sign in the other. Ask the children, one by one, to place their card in the correct hoop. To reinforce their learning swap some cards over in the hoops and ask the children to correct the hoops.

- Ask the children to work in with their chatting chum. Give each pair a problem to solve. Prepare large laminated word problems (A4 size). Ask the children to circle the vocabulary that will help them solve the problem. Once they have established what type of sum it is ask the children to solve the word problem.

cards with pictures of bad characters from fairy tales, for example the Big Bad Wolf, wicked witch, troll, giant. The children take it in turns to pick out a problem and try to solve it. Once they have found the answer, they must cover the appropriate number on the board. If they pick out a danger card they must remove all the cards on their board. The winner is the child who has covered the most numbers on their board.

Practical Activities

- The children pick a fairy tale and write a number story relating to that fairy tale. The children use illustrations instead of certain words. For example, 'Once upon a time in a wood there were three bears. They each had four cakes to eat. How many cakes did they have altogether?' The children could draw and colour the number of bears and cakes.
- Play 'Race and Ring'. Pre-make a large selection of problem cards. Give each child a whiteboard and pen. Place a bell in the middle of the table. Read out a word problem and the children must race to write down the correct sum and answer it on their board. Once they have the correct answer, they must ring the bell. If they are correct they receive a point.
- Play 'Story Squares'. Make a lotto-style board for each child in the group with numbers 1 to 10 on it. Make a large selection of number problems that have the answers 1 to 10. Place the cards in a bag or box. Also include some danger

Art and Display Ideas

- Using newspaper ask the children to cut out and collage numbers onto black paper. Encourage the children to rotate the numbers so they are not uniform.
- Give each child a large cut-out number. Invite them to decorate their number using fairy tales as a stimulus. Use wax crayons, felt pens or oil pastels to create a colourful look.
- Using *The Snail* (1952–1953) by Henri Matisse as inspiration, the children choose a number, decorate it using collage material, then cut it out and place it on a black background. Encourage the children to overlap the numbers.
- Finger-painting numbers – Chalk pastel the background and ask the children to finger paint numbers on top of the background.

Cross-curricular Links

- **ICT** – Using the digital camera, children should take photographs of themselves. Using a photo package they can turn themselves into a character from a fairy tale.
- **Literacy** – Ask the children to create their own version of a fairy tale but challenge them to change the characters. For example, instead of the three bears they could tell a story about three monkeys.
- **D&T** – Using recyclable materials invite the children to build a fairy tale castle.

The Not So Noble Knight

Whole-class Starter

- Use a programmable toy (a Roamer or a Bee-Bot™) that has been turned into a knight. Sit the children in a circle and tell them a story about the knight who could not locate his possessions because he did not know which direction to turn. Ask the children what they know about turns and put some words on the board, for example 'clockwise', 'anticlockwise', 'half turn', 'quarter turn', 'whole turn' (depending on the children's ability you could also include '90 degrees', '180 degrees' and '360 degrees'). Discuss with the children what they understand by these words and say that, if they use them correctly, they can help the knight find his possessions. Place the knight's possessions around the programmable toy. Choose one of the knight's possessions and ask the children to program the toy correctly. This can be repeated several times.

Focus of Learning
To understand the difference between clockwise and anticlockwise turns

- Play 'The Knight's Quest'. Make a set of laminated grids with pictures of the knight's possessions in several of the squares. Place a picture of the knight in one of the squares. Ask the children to work with a partner and give each child a board and a pen. Tell the children that the knight needs to find his possessions and they must help him complete his quest by following the instructions. Read out a set of instructions. For example, 'Move two squares forward, turn half a turn anticlockwise and move three squares. What possession have you found?' The children use the pen to mark the knight's route and find the correct possession.
- Play 'The Knight Says'. This is based on the game 'Simon Says'. Put on a knight's outfit and give instructions to the children to follow. For example, 'The knight says turn clockwise quarter of a turn.' The children carry out the instruction.

Practical Activities

- Play 'Direct It'. The children work in pairs and one child wears a blindfold. Place a number of objects around the room or large space. The children must direct their partner to an object using the directional language – 'clockwise', 'anticlockwise', 'half turn', 'quarter turn', 'whole turn' (depending on ability you could also include '90 degrees', '180 degrees' and '360 degrees').
- Play 'Racing Robot'. For this game you will need at least two or three programmable toys. Create identical grids for each toy. All over each grid place pictures of the knight's possessions. Also make a set of picture cards of the knight's possessions and the children must program the toy correctly so the first toy to reach the object wins a point for the team.

- Play 'Race for the Route'. Make a large grid using either carpet mats or hoops (36 squares would be a good number). Place several of the knight's possessions on the mats or in the hoops. On a given signal stand in the start hoop and say, 'I am the not so noble knight and I am looking for my... sword, horse, castle, and so on.' The children must write down the correct instructions for the knight to follow. The first child to complete the instructions rings a bell, and if correct the child gets a point.

Display Ideas

- Using Mondrian as inspiration draw and paint a castle.
- Draw and paint colourful castles.
- Paint and collage a large knight for display.
- Paint and collage items associated with a knight, for example a horse, dragon, armour, lance, princess.
- Design and paint a shield to use as a border for the display.
- Using the inspiration of Colin Thompson draw and paint a castle using different objects. For example, use leaves and call it *The Leaf* or sports equipment and so on.

Cross-curricular Links

- **Literacy** – Draw, pen and colour a picture of a knight and write facts about knights around him.
- **Maths** – Using pictures of 3D shapes work as a group to cut out and stick the shapes to make a castle collage. Chalk pastel the castle to give colour.
- **Geography** – Draw a map of the knight's kingdom and write some instructions to help him travel around.

Numberella Umbrella

Whole-class Starter

- Enter the classroom as Mrs Numberella, carrying an umbrella with raindrops hanging from it. Each raindrop has a number on it. Place several puddles on the floor that have number patterns on but each pattern has a number missing. Ask the children to help you locate the correct puddle for each raindrop. Ask the children to work with a chatting chum. Give them a laminated sheet with puddles on and ask the children to look at the patterns and put in the missing raindrop number. Discuss their answers and put the correct raindrop onto each puddle.

- Play 'Raindrop Reveal'. Make a laminated raindrop for

Focus of Learning
Number patterns/sequences

each child. Prepare an IWB display that has raindrops falling, each raindrop has a number. One of the raindrops has a number missing. The children must work out the pattern or sequence of the numbers, work out the answer and write it on their own raindrop. The children hold up the raindrop and reveal the answer to the teacher or Mrs Numberella. Discuss with the children how they calculated the answer.

- Play 'Raindrop Racing'. This game will need to be played in the hall or a large classroom area.

Make a set of large puddles with the solution to various number sequences. For example +7, −4, doubling, halving. Place these puddles around the hall. Make sets of raindrops with number patterns or sequences on. You will need lots of raindrops – five for each pair of children. The object of the game is for the children to move around the hall and race to place their raindrops in the correct puddle. The first pair to correctly place all their raindrops is the winner.

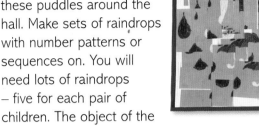

Practical Activities

- Play 'Rainy Roulette'. Make a selection of laminated umbrellas with number pattern problems on. The object of the game is for the children to solve the problems within a given time. Use a plastic bottle to spin and if the child has not completed the number pattern before the bottle stops spinning they are faced with a rainy forfeit; raindrops are gently dropped on the child's head!
- Play 'Numberella Umbrella'. Use a large open umbrella and place it in the middle of a table or carpet area. Make a selection of laminated raindrops with number patterns on. Split the children into two teams. The first team has to work out as many raindrop sequence patterns as possible within a minute, write them on an

answer sheet and place the solved raindrops in the umbrella. The opposite team must then check the answers. Then the teams swap over. The team with the most correct completed raindrops wins the game.

- Play 'Puzzle Puddle'. Ask the children to work with a partner and on a laminated puddle-shaped piece of paper they write a number pattern for their friend to work out.

Art and Display Ideas

- Paint a giant umbrella and Mrs Numberella for the display.
- Research the artist David Hockney and reproduce a water picture in his style.
- What is water? Using magazines, clip art and their own artistic skills, ask the children to create a collaged picture depicting different uses for water.
- Using a raindrop shape, layer the raindrop with different media to make a 3D water drop then hang it from the display.

- Bring in a selection of umbrellas and ask the children to sketch them.
- Make a clay umbrella and on each section make a different pattern using a range of clay tools.

Cross-curricular Links

- **Science** – Learn about different types of weather and the effect it has on people's everyday lives.
- **Literacy** – Listen to a prepared tape with different sounds of rain, for example gentle rain, thunderstorm, torrential. Write an onomatopoeic rain poem.
- **PSHCE** – Read the story *A Necklace of Raindrops* by Joan Aiken, and Jan Pieńkowski (Jonathan Cape 2009). Discuss the actions of Meg from the story. What would the children do if they had Laura's powers?

Off With Your Head!

Whole-class Starter

- The class receives a DVD from Henry VIII, which you have prepared. Henry tells the children that the true reason for beheading his wives was not because he was an evil man but because they simply did not know how to use their heads to perform maths mentally. He explains that if they have no use for their heads then they must be removed! 'Off with their heads, I said, and this will happen to you if you are unable to use your heads for mental calculations. Children of Britain prepare yourself for battle. You must use your heads mentally to perform the following calculations. If you fail, you know the consequences.'

Focus of Learning
To be able to tackle a range of mental maths problems and explain the strategies used

- Henry explains that he is not an unreasonable man so you may have a few chances to practise your skills before he begins. He presents the children with a mental problem. For example, 'Find the product of 12 and 7' (the difficulty will depend on the children's ability). Henry then talks through how to solve the problem using his head. He repeats this several times.

- Play 'Heads Together'. Prepare a set of scrolls with individual mental problems on. Split the class into teams and place a bell in the middle of the room. Give each team a whiteboard and a pen and a copy of the first problem. The children must work together to solve the problem. They must write the answer on their whiteboard and once finished send a team member to ring the bell. The last team to answer correctly is out. Talk through the problem before introducing the next one. The last team standing are the winners, and get to keep their heads!

Practical Activities

- Play 'Off With Your Head'. In a small group give a mental maths problem (group children according to ability and make questions ability-appropriate). Children must work the answer out mentally and shout it out. The

person who gets the answer correct first can nominate another player and says, 'Off with their head!' which means they are out. Repeat several times. The last child standing is the winner.

- Play 'Henry's Headaches'. Use a prepared tape or CD of recorded maths problems read out by Henry VIII. Give the children a time limit before the next question begins. At the end of the tape go through the questions and discuss strategies and misconceptions.

- Play 'Beheaded'. Make a set of

laminated boards with pictures of Henry VIII's wives on it – there should be one for each child. Make a set of cards with mental maths problems on them and also picture-cards of Henry VIII. The children take it in turns to pick out a card and solve the sum mentally. If they are successful, great! If they are incorrect they must behead one of the wives by crossing her out with a marker pen. If they pick a Henry VIII card they are allowed to behead a wife from another child's board. The object is to keep all of the wives safe from being beheaded.

Art and Display Ideas

- Paint, collage or chalk-pastel a large Henry VIII for a display.
- The children can paint watercolours of Henry VIII's wives in the style of Hans Holbein.
- Using a layering technique, create a clay Tudor rose.
- Create a ripped paper Tudor rose.
- Using fabric, felt and threads make a Tudor rose.

Cross-curricular Links

- **History** – Research the Tudor family tree. Create a display to use as a teaching tool for the children.
- **ICT** – Create a Tudor rose using an art package on the computer.
- **Literacy** – Debate whether Henry VIII was a good or bad king. This could be carried out as an oral debate, a written debate or both.

53

A Midsummer Night's Dream

Whole-class Starter

- Enter the classroom as Puck. Explain that within the magical woods where you live two love-struck couples came wandering recently and their love has been all mixed up because of your magic in which you have used the four mathematical rules to create mischief and mayhem. Using the IWB, show pictures of the characters and explain what has happened to their love. For example Demetrius' love has been *taken away* by Lysander. Hermia's love is *divided* between Demetrius and Lysander. Helena's love has been *multiplied* and now she does not know who to love and Lysander's love for Hermia has been *added* to Helena. On the board reveal the four different signs and corresponding words. For example '+,' 'add,' 'total,' 'altogether,' etc.

Focus of Learning
To understand and begin to use the four rules to solve word problems

- Play 'Puck's Puzzles'. Split the class into equal teams. Give each team a mat to sit on and a large piece of paper or whiteboard to write on. Puck reveals a problem on the IWB. The children must solve the problem as a team, including showing their working out, which they must write on their board or piece of paper. When they have finished they must ring a bell. As a class, discuss the problems and how they were solved and the different ways they worked them out. The winning team gets a sprinkle of fairy dust and the losing team is eliminated.

Practical Activities

There are 120 trees in the forest. Each tree has 15 fairy lights on it. How many lights are there in total?

Titania has 17 servants. She gives each servant 9 jobs. How many jobs altogether?

Lysander and Hermia run for 95 minutes. They rest for 126 minutes and then run for another 58 minutes. How many minutes have they run for?

- Play 'Mischief and Mayhem'. Make two sets of identical fairy cards with word problems on and two sets of leaves with the corresponding answers on. Also include some blank leaves and some extra fairy problems and tell the children that Puck has been playing some mischief and left some leaves blank. Place the cards on two large boards or wall. Split the group into two teams and allocate each team a board. The children must solve the word problems and match them to the correct leaf. They then must solve the extra problems and write the answers on the blank leaves. The first team to complete all the problems and match the answers correctly to the leaves is the winner.
- Play 'Puck's Pandemonium'. Make a set of addition, multiplication, subtraction and division signs and place them on the walls around a large space. Give each child a whiteboard and a pen. Make a set of laminated cards with problems written on them. Give each child a card and on a given signal they must solve the problem using one of the four rules. Once they have solved the problem they must run to the sign that they used to solve their problem. The child who reaches the correct sign first wins a point.
- Play 'Midsummer's Madness'. Make a set of laminated fairy cards with word problems on and hide them among the trees in an environmental area. Give each child a pair of fairy wings and a magic fairy pen. On the given signal the children flutter off and try to find as many cards as possible. They must solve the problem and take it back to you to check. The child who collects and solves the most fairy cards correctly is the winner.

Art and Display Ideas

- Using Rousseau as an inspiration, create a magical or enchanted wood picture using a fabric background and collage effect. Build the picture up to create a 3D effect.
- Create a fairy silhouette picture. Chalk-pastel or paint the purple background. Chalk-pastel the Moon onto the background. Cut out a black silhouette tree and fairy and stick them to the background.
- Give each child a fairy template and ask the children to cut out white or silver pieces of paper and place on the fairy to create wing veins.
- Create a 3D flower garden using mesh, plastic bags and the bottom of plastic bottles.
- Pick a selection of leaves for the children to use. The children place the leaves in different positions and directions on the paper. They draw around the leaves and paint them using autumn colours. The children use black paint to create a leaf vein effect. Use this for the background for display.

Cross-curricular Links

- **Literacy** – Read a simple version of *A Midsummer Night's Dream* by William Shakespeare and ask the children to draw a map of the characters' relationships.
- **History** – Learn about the theatre in Tudor times. Compare Shakespeare's theatre to the modern theatre of today.
- **History** – Research the life of William Shakespeare.

Division Divers

10 divers fit onto each lifeboat. How many lifeboats would I need to carry 72 divers?

8 fish fit into each bucket. How many buckets would I need to carry 68 fish?

What operation do you need to use to solve all of these problems?

6 sails fit onto each mast. How many masts would I need for 47 sails?

A money pouch can hold 7 pearls. How many pouches would I need to hold 43 pearls?

Can you decide whether to round up or down after dividing?

A treasure chest holds 9 bars of gold. How many treasure chests can I fill completely with 57 bars of gold?

7 fishing rods fit into each cupboard. How many cupboards would I need to hold 29 fishing rods?

All of the answers to these questions must be whole numbers because the answers are people, animals or objects.

6 divers can sleep in one cabin. How many full cabins do I have if there are 34 divers on the ship?

9 crabs can fit into 1 chiller box. How many boxes would I need to hold 65 crabs?

Whole-class Starter

- Play 'Sink that Ship'. The objective of this activity is to recap on mental division to ensure the children understand the concept. Split the class into teams of four and give each team a ship's name, such as *Titanic* or *Mary Rose*. One child from each team must stand up. Pose a division problem for the children to solve mentally such as 56 ÷ 8 or 50 ÷ 7. The child that answers first chooses a ship to sink. Continue until one ship remains, which is the winner!

Focus of Learning
To know when to round up or round down after division

- Give each team the same problem: 'There are 38 people stranded on a desert island. Six people fit in each rescue boat. How many lifeboats would be needed to rescue everybody from the island?' Ask the children to discuss their answers and

their reasons for the answers. Establish that the amount of boats needed is seven because we don't want to leave any people behind. Explain that you have rounded up the answer to enable everyone to be rescued from the island but that sometimes in division you can round down the answer. Illustrate by showing them another problem: 'The sailors catch 42 fish. Five fish fit into a net. How many nets would they fill completely?' Discuss the answer and why this is rounding down. Give the teams several more problems in which they must decide whether to round up or round down the answer.

- Play 'Up or Down'. Prepare a set of word problems on the IWB which include a range of rounding up and rounding down problems similar to those above. The children must either stand up if they think you need to divide and round up, or stay sitting if you need to divide and round down. Discuss the children's responses and any misconceptions.

Practical Activities

- Play 'Fish for It!'. You will need a magnetic fishing set and some fishing nets for this game. Stick problems involving rounding up or down on each magnetic fish. The children take it in turns to fish for a problem. If they answer correctly they keep the fish and place it in their fishing net. The child with the most fish at the end of the game wins.
- Play 'Division Divers'. Make a set of fish with numbers on. Place the fish in a water tray or paddling pool. The children take it in turns to wear a snorkel mask and 'dive' for a fish. Then they must write a word problem on a whiteboard which involves rounding up

or down and the number they have picked. (This activity must be supervised by an adult.)

- Play 'Sink or Swim'. Give each group a snorkel mask. Make a circle around a water tray or paddling pool. The children take it turns to pick a prepared problem. They must decide if it is a rounding up or rounding down problem. If it is rounding up they are safe and stay afloat but if they have a rounding down problem they must 'sink' and put their head in the water! (This activity must be supervised by an adult.)

Art and Display Ideas

- Draw and colour a detailed picture of a Tudor ship.
- Use pen and ink to draw a Tudor ship.
- Using art straws, recreate the *Mary Rose*.
- Using inspiration from the work of Fernard Leger, recreate *The Big Black Divers* (1944). The children should draw and oil-pastel pictures of deep-sea divers and create a collage on a black background.

Cross-curricular Links

- **History** – Learn about the sinking of the *Mary Rose* during Tudor times.
- **History** – Learn about life on a Tudor ship and the different jobs that people did on board.
- **Literacy** – Write a poem about the sinking of the *Mary Rose*. Write two contrasting stanzas that describe the scene when the *Mary Rose* set sail and then the scene as she began to sink. Include similes, alliteration, powerful verbs and metaphor.
- **Science** – Investigate the displacement of water during floating and sinking.

Proper and Improper Fractions

Whole-class Starter

- Explain to the children that they are going to learn about three types of fractions. But before they start they need to establish what they already know about fractions. Using the IWB show the children a selection of pictorial fractions. Ask the children to identify the fractions. Discuss what part of the fraction is needed in order to make it a whole.

- Play 'Proper or Improper'. On the IWB create a slideshow that has two walls. One which looks like a graffiti wall and one that looks like a non-graffiti wall. On the graffiti wall write

Focus of Learning
To recognise what proper, improper and mixed numbers are and to be able to convert improper fractions to mixed fractions

the word 'improper' and on the non-graffiti wall write the word 'proper'. Give each child a paddle with red on one side and green on the other. A fraction pops up on the board. If the children think it is a proper fraction they show the red side of the paddle, and if they think it is improper they show the green side. Once the children have decided reveal the answer on the IWB. To extend this activity give each child a sticky-note and ask them to write a proper or improper fraction and place it on the correct wall on the IWB (this will check their understanding).

- After the children have established what

improper and proper fractions look like, play 'The Art of Fractions'. Show the children a fraction and ask them to draw it pictorially.

- Tell the children that you are going to show them a third type of fraction. Introduce the term 'mixed fraction' and show them an example, such as 1½. Discuss with the children that an improper fraction can be changed into a mixed fraction. Give them some examples: $^3/_2$ becomes 1½ or $^5/_4$ becomes 1¼. Play 'Mix and Match' using the green and red paddles. Create a slideshow display which flashes up two fractions. If the fractions match the children show the green side of the paddle. If they do not match they show the red side.

Practical Activities

- Play 'Rainbow Fractions'. Place a large piece of paper with a mixed fraction written on in the middle of each table. Give each child a set of sticky-notes. The children move around the classroom visiting each mixed fraction. At each mixed fraction the children must write an equivalent improper fraction on a sticky-note and stick it onto the large piece of paper. Give the children a set time to get rid of all their sticky-notes.
- Play 'Bucket Bonanza'. Give each child a bucket with a different mixed fraction on the front. Make a large amount of improper fractions that match the mixed fractions. Hide these all around the school or classroom. On a given signal the children must race to find all the improper fractions that are equivalent to their mixed fraction.
- Play 'Finding Fractions'. Make a set of laminated searchword-style boards with improper and mixed fractions all over it. Give each child in the group a board and ten different-coloured whiteboard pens. On a given signal the children must race to circle an improper and mixed fraction that correspond with each other. They must use

a different-coloured pen for each pair. The child who finds ten equivalent fractions is the winner. This could be a timed activity.

Art and Display Ideas

- Using graffiti as inspiration help the children to create a graffiti wall in school.
- Using card, paint and collage materials the children can create their own graffiti wall to use on the display.
- Using classic pieces of art to symbolise 'proper' art ask the children to draw, paint and chalk some classic pieces of artwork. For example, *Mona Lisa* by da Vinci (1503), *Sunflowers* by Monet (1881), *The Snail* by Matisse (1952–1953), *Still Life, Drapery, Pitcher and Fruit Bowl* by Cezanne (1893–1894).

Cross-curricular Links

- **Art** – Study art through the decades and how it has changed and what brought about these varying art forms. Look at Vorticism, cubism, surrealism, for example.
- **Art** – Study the history of graffiti and how it has progressed from an antisocial action to an art form. Look at the work of Banksy.

Find a Shape

Whole-class Starter

- Enter the classroom to the *Pink Panther* music in the role of Jacques Columbo, or the class could receive a DVD from him. Explain that you are the local shape detective and recently somebody has been sabotaging the shapes. Show the children the evidence using your special IWB. Reveal an irregular shape and ask the children to look carefully at the shape and with a chatting chum, discuss the clues they see to decide what the shape might be. For example, reveal a six-sided irregular shape. The children inform Jacques Columbo that the shape has six sides and six corners but the sides are all different lengths. Ask the children if they know what shape it could be from the clues given. Reveal the possible suspects on the board. Display the regular shapes on the board and as a class identify and name the shapes. The children look at the shapes' properties to try to identify the irregular

Focus of Learning
To begin to identify irregular shapes

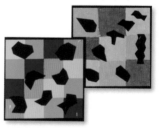

shape. As a class they discover the irregular shape is a hexagon and they discuss why. This can be repeated several times.

- Jacques Columbo reveals to the children that the secret to discovering the irregular shapes is to know your regular shapes really well. He gives each pair a laminated board with all the regular shapes on. He explains that he is going to give the children a clue and they must try to identify the shape. Using the IWB show the children a clue (a property of a shape). The children must circle which shape they think it is and name it. Discuss any misconceptions.

- Play 'Find a Shape'. Use the same board as the carpet session but ensure there is a number 1 to 15 on the opposite side. Make a large set of irregular laminated shapes numbered 1 to 15 and hide them around the school. Send each pair of children off with their board to find their irregular shape. They should identify the shape and then return to the class. As a class discuss what they discovered. The children can swap boards and repeat this activity.

Practical Activities

- Using the activity from the carpet session. Replay 'Find the Shape'. Send the children off around the school independently with a grid numbered 1 to 15. The children must find each shape, identify it and write the name in the correct numbered space.
- Play 'Detect and Draw'. Make a board for each child with blank squares on. The squares need to big enough for a shape to be drawn in. Make a spinner with words of regular shapes written on. Include on the spinner a picture of a swag bag and a picture of Jacques Columbo. The children take it in turns to spin the spinner. If they land on a shape they must read the word, identify the shape and draw it as an irregular shape in one of the boxes. If they land on the swag bag they must rub out one of their shapes and if they land on Jacques Columbo they can draw an irregular shape on their board.
- Play 'Matching Mystery'. Base this game on Pelmanism. Make two sets of different-coloured laminated cards. One set shows regular shapes and the other set shows irregular shapes. Include several Jacques

Columbo cards. The children take it in turns to pick up two cards, one of each colour. If they pick a pair, for example a regular pentagon and an irregular pentagon, they keep the cards, if not they must replace them on the table. The object is to collect the most pairs. If they pick a detective card they are allowed to take a pair from another player in the game. The winner is the child with the most pairs of cards at the end.

Art and Display Ideas

- Paint and collage a large Jacques Columbo.
- Using oil pastels create a chequered background. The children should draw and collage irregular shapes onto the background.
- Using collage materials cut out squares from two different-coloured pieces of paper and create a chequered background. The children should draw and collage irregular shapes onto the background.
- Using bright colours on a black background, collage irregular shapes. Encourage the children to place shapes on top of each other to create a 3D effect.

Cross-curricular Links

- **Art** – Using Picasso as inspiration, create a face using irregular shapes.
- **ICT** – Using a computer, import regular shapes into a *Word*® document. The children take two of the same shape and by overlapping and moving the shapes they must recreate an irregular shape. Import a background and add colour with a paint package.
- **Literacy** – Look at the genre of mystery stories. Identify the common features.

Decimoles

On the display:

We helped Decimole put his mole hills in order.

We met Decimole.

He is the mole who lives in the little black hole you see sometimes between numbers.

His hole is called a decimal point.

Can you read the decimals on Decimole's mole hills?

A decimal p[...] separates a [...] number from parts of a number.

1.1 1.3 1.4 1.6 1.7 1.9

Whole-class Starter

- Dress up as a mole (or use a puppet). Explain that your name is Decimole, and that you are the mole who lives between whole numbers in a little black hole called a decimal. Ask the children if they know what a decimal point is and why they might use them. Explain that they are often used during measurements so that you can be accurate. A decimal point separates the whole number from the parts of numbers. On the IWB, show the children a large number 1 on one side of the board and a large number 2 on the other side. Explain that decimoles live between these big numbers. On the IWB produce small molehills between the numbers. Ask the children what the number would be on the first molehill (1.1), and so on.

Focus of Learning
To be able to read decimal numbers correctly and to begin to order decimals

- Decimole tells the children that he has a very clever way to remember. He reveals his favourite chocolate bar, a Toblerone. He shows one whole bar and then he reveals a second bar which has been split into sections. He holds up one whole bar and a single piece and asks the children what this would be as a number. On the IWB he reveals the answer 1.1.

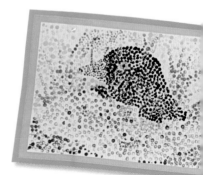

He explains that this is one whole bar and a bit – the decimal point represents the smaller bit. He repeats this several times. He holds up a whole Toblerone and a number of pieces and the children must write it down as a decimal. The children should share their answers and any misconceptions should be discussed. (Check for any known food allergies before foodstuffs are used in classroom activities.)

- Explain to the children that decimals always follow a certain order by showing how they fit on a number line. Play 'Manic Moles'. Make a set of molehills with decimals from 1.1 to 2 on. Make three sets in different colours so that you have enough for each child in the class. Each child should have one card and on a given signal the children must find their team (the other children with the same-colour card) and arrange themselves in the correct order. The winning team wins a piece of Decimole's favourite chocolate.

- Display three number lines on the IWB. The line should show whole numbers and decimals (for example, 1–2, 2–3, 3–4). But on each line there should be some whole numbers and some decimals missing. The children should redraw the lines on paper and, in pairs, work out the numbers and decimals that are missing on each line.

Practical Activities

- Play 'Dash for the Decimals'. Make a set of laminated decimal numbers that can be ordered. In a large area create a mole obstacle course using small tunnels. Place the numbers on a large board at the end of the obstacle course.

Split the children into two groups and give each child a mole nose to wear. Give each group two whole numbers and the object is for the children to collect the correct decimals that go between the whole numbers. On a given signal the children take it in turns to tackle the obstacle course and collect a decimal. They come back to their team and put the decimal in the correct place between the two whole numbers.

- Play 'Molehills'. Make a set of laminated boards with five molehills in a line. Make a set of decimal cards and place them in a box. Give each child in the group a board. Also place a mole nose and glasses in the middle of the table. The children take it in turns to pick out five decimal cards and place them face down on the table. On a given signal the children must turn over their five decimal cards and place them in the correct order on their board. The first child to order their cards correctly must put on the mole nose and glasses and they are the winner.

Art and Display Ideas

- Using Dubuffet for inspiration ask the children to begin their work by creating a large decimal point and create a doodle art effect. They can colour it using felt pens (blue, red and black). Put a border around the work that complements the colours.
- Using the inspiration of African Pointillist art, recreate a mole-style picture.
- Using chalk pastels the children can draw their own mole in different poses. Use it for display.

Cross-curricular Links

- **PE and Maths** – Using PE equipment set up a tunnelling session. Introduce problem-solving activities within the tunnelling exercise. For example, in the tunnels they should find jigsaw pieces with decimals on. Each child should find one and as a team put them in the correct order.
- **Science** – Investigate the habitats of a range of animals, including moles.
- **Maths** – Investigate where decimals are used in everyday life and why, for example the depth of a swimming pool.

All Sorts

Whole-class Starter

- Explain to the children that they are going to be learning about converting all sorts of things. Ask the children what conversion or converting means? Discuss the answer and agree with the class a common definition. Explain that they are going to be converting all sorts of things – fractions, decimals and percentages. Have with you two packets of Liquorice Allsorts, one of which is full of questions and the other full of sweets. Explain to the children that in order to convert a question into a sweet they must answer the question correctly. Ask a range of questions related to converting percentages, decimals and fractions.
- Play 'Bertie's Brain-teaser'. Using the IWB prepare a board full of Allsorts sweet shapes with some sweets having fractions on and the others with the equivalent decimals. Ask the children to work with a partner and write the pairs of conversions on a whiteboard. Repeat this exercise but include percentages. Ask the children to match all three variations and once again record these on a whiteboard and discuss them.
- Play 'Conversion Conundrum'. On the IWB prepare some large pictures of sweets that will appear one at a time. Each sweet should have on it a 'conversion conundrum' such as 25% or 0.75 or $^{1}/_{10}$. When a picture appears the children must convert it any way they like, write it on a whiteboard and hold it up. The quickest conversion wins a sweet. You could extend this game by challenging the children to see who can convert in the most different ways.

Focus of Learning
To learn how to convert fractions, decimals and percentages

Practical Activities

- Play 'Bertie's Bingo'. Prepare a set of bingo boards with a range of different fractions, decimals and percentages on. In a bag prepare cards with the equivalent fractions, decimals and percentages on, together with some Bertie Bassett cards. If the children pull out a number card they may cover up the appropriate conversion. If they pull out a Bertie Bassett card they are allowed to eat a sweet. (Check for any known food allergies before foodstuffs are used in classroom activities.)

- Play 'Build a Bertie'. Make several sets of Liquorice Allsorts that make up Bertie Bassett. On each part of Bertie Bassett write a decimal, fraction or percentage. The object of the game is for each child to build their own Bertie Bassett by collecting Bertie Bassett pieces. Each team takes it in turn to pick out a piece of Bertie Bassett. They must write down the two conversions that match the piece of Bertie Bassett in order to keep the piece and build Bertie.

- Play 'Sweet Swap'. This game is based on 'Old Maid'. Make a set of cards that have four equivalent values, for example 0.25, $^{25}/_{100}$, ¼, 25%. Deal out the cards so that each player has four cards. The players must pass one card around the circle at a time and the idea is to convert their cards into the perfect family.

Art and Display Ideas

- Draw Bertie Bassett and paint him with watercolour pencils.
- Make clay Bertie Bassetts.

- Using Liquorice Allsorts™ create a new Allsorts character. Ask the children to come up with a suitable name for their character.
- Build a giant Bertie Bassett out of recyclable materials.

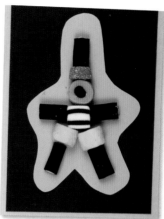

Cross-curricular Links

- **D&T** – Design and make a moving convertible vehicle. Focus on the mechanism used to 'convert' the vehicle, and discuss physical changes.
- **Science** – Change or convert materials, for example solid to liquid, liquid to gas, chemical changes, reversible and irreversible changes.

Tick Tock, What's on the Clock?

Whole-class Starter

- Enter the classroom as Mr Wolf and explain to the children that today you are here to teach them how to tell the time. Begin by playing 'What's the time Mr Wolf?'. The children chant the sentence. On the IWB reveal a large clock showing a time. Begin with o'clock, quarter past, half past and quarter to. Explain that you think it is about time the children started to play a game with a bit more of a challenge. Explain that you are going to teach them how to tell the time in five-minute intervals. Ask the children to count in five forwards and backwards. Tap individual children on the head and they must stand up and say 5, 10, 15 and so on up to 60. Bring up an empty number line on the IWB and ask the children if they can use it to count in fives. Reveal the numbers to check if they are correct. Change the line into a circle and ask the children if they can still count in fives. Put symbols on the clock and ask the children if the symbols confuse them. Display a clock face on the IWB showing the numbers 1 to 12. Ask the children to count in fives around the circle. Do the numbers 1 to 12 confuse them? Add a big hand and a small hand to the circle to create a clock.

Focus of Learning
To learn to tell the time in five-minute intervals and to understand 'to' and 'past'

- Play 'What's the time Mr Wolf?'. Mr Wolf gives each child a clock. On a given signal the children ask the question, 'What's the time Mr Wolf?' Mr Wolf tells the children a 'past' time, for

create and display: **Mathematics**

example 5 past 1, 20 past 4. The children must move the hands on the clock to show the time and show Mr Wolf the answer. He reveals the correct time on a giant clock on the IWB. Mr Wolf could throw in quarter past and discuss with the children that this is the same as 15 minutes past but we say it differently. Similarly he could discuss half past and 30 minutes past.

- Mr Wolf reveals on the IWB a giant clock that has been split into two halves. One side is coloured red and one side is blue. Mr Wolf has labelled his clock with all the correct vocabulary, 'o'clock', 'quarter past', 'half past' and 'quarter to'. He explains to the children that once the minute hand goes past the six, the language we use becomes 'to' not 'past'. He counts around the clock from 'o'clock' and reveals the five-minute intervals on the 'past' side. He stops at half past, goes back to the 'o'clock' and reveals five-minute intervals on the 'to' side, going backwards to half past.

Practical Activities

- In a large area make a giant clock on the floor. Mr Wolf reveals a time on the board and the children must initially make the time on a small

clock and then as a group work together to make the time on the giant clock. Mr Wolf reveals the answer.

- Play 'Losing Lives'. Make a set of laminated wolf cards with times written on. Make a set of small wolf cards, enough for three for each child. Give each child a clock and three lives. The children take a wolf card out of the box, read the time, add on five-minutes to that time and display it on their clock. Check the answers and if the children are incorrect they lose a wolf life (one small wolf card taken away). Once all their lives have gone they are out of the game. The winner is the child who survives the longest. An extension to this game could be to add 10 or 15 minute intervals to their time.

Art and Display Ideas

- Using the inspiration of Salvador Dali create a distorted clock out of clay.
- Paint a clock face using black paint and using a brush swirl over the wet clock face to create a distorted effect.
- Using watercolour paint to create a background, draw a distorted clock using a second colour and paint it with a different colour.
- Using oil pastels draw the sunshine and split it into four sections. Each section must be coloured to represent different stages in the day, for example, blues and purples for night- time, yellows and oranges for the hottest time of the day.
- Investigate colours that represent different parts of the day. Create a background using chalk pastels. Turn this into a clock face.

Cross-curricular Links

- **History** – Looking at the passing of time – past, present, and future – ask the children to pick an object and research how that object has changed over time. Look at, for example, a washing machine or bicycle.
- **Literacy** – Using *The Bad-Tempered Ladybird* by Eric Carle (Puffin, 2010) as a stimulus, ask the children to write their own version using times that have five-minute intervals.

All About Averages

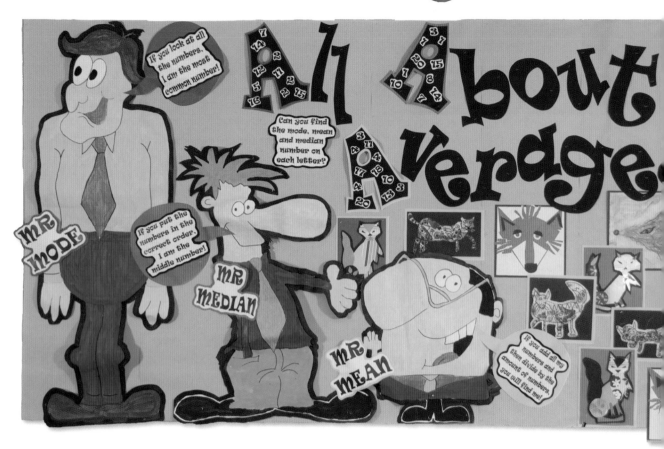

Whole-class Starter

- The class receives a DVD or a letter from Mr Mode, Mr Mean and Mr Median. On the DVD or in the letter they explain their methods for working out the average of numbers or data. They argue among themselves about whose method is the best. To help the children remember they teach the children a song:

MODE
MEDIAN
MEAN
One common
One middle
One unseen
These unusual names
So different their aims
Will help the averages come clean!!!

- Mr Mode, Mr Mean and Mr Median finish by setting the children some challenges to

Focus of Learning
To understand averages and how to calculate the mode, mean and median of a group of numbers

complete. Using a prepared slideshow reveal a set of data (which includes a mode, for example 7 3 5 7 7 2 9) for a week. Ask the children to find either the mode, mean or median (or all three).

- Play 'Splat an Egg'. Prepare a board with eggs on. On each egg place a number. The numbers on the eggs will be the answers to the children's problems. Split the class into threes or fours. Give each group a

basket of numbers. One of the farmer's faces appears on the board: Mr Mode, Mr Mean or Mr Median. The children take the numbers out of their basket and work together to find the answer according to the farmer. Once they have the answer they must splat the correct egg on the board.

Practical Activities

- Play 'Eggspert Hunt'. Using small plastic eggs, place a set of numbers in each egg. Hide the eggs around the classroom, school or outside area. The children must find an egg, open it and using the numbers inside the egg find the mode, mean and median.
- Play 'Chicken Run'. Make a set of laminated cards with a row of numbers on and an average number in a different colour (you will need lots of cards). You will need a basket of plastic eggs. Ensure that there is a range of numbers on the cards.
- Place a bell at the front of the classroom. Split the group into twos or threes. Give each group the same laminated card. The children must race to discover if the average is the mode, mean or median. Once they have found the answer they race to ring the bell. The group who rings the bell first collects an egg. The group with the most eggs wins the game.

- Make a selection of real-life word problems using bar charts and measures. For example,

'Mr Mode weighs 94kg, Mr Mean weighs 16kg, Mr Median weighs 39kg. What is the mean average?' See how many problems the children can solve in five minutes. Discuss the answers and any misconceptions that may have occurred.

Art and Display Ideas

- Draw, paint and collage pictures of Mr Mean, Mr Mode and Mr Median. Base the characters on Mr Bean, Mr Boggis and Mr Bunce from the story *Fantastic Mr Fox* by Roald Dahl (Puffin, 2007).
- Using textiles such as felt, fabric and feathers, glue a fox picture.
- Using paper and the ripping technique create a picture of a fox.
- Using brown parcel paper and chalk pastels create a picture of a fox's head.
- Using newspaper and black paper collage a picture of a fox.
- Using wrapping paper and magazines, collage a picture of a fox.

Cross-curricular Links

- **Literacy** – The children read and learn all about the author Roald Dahl. You could read his autobiographies *Boy* and *Going Solo* (both Puffin, 2008) to find out more about his life.
- **ICT** – Collect a variety of data and using an ICT package present them in bar charts, pie charts and so on.
- **Science** – Look at food chains, using foxes as a starting point.

69

Awesome Angles

Whole-class Starter

- Enter the classroom as the Angle Angel. Explain to the children that you love angles and ask if they know what an angle is. Check that the children can define an angle as the point where two lines meet and that you can measure the angles in degrees using a protractor. Explain that today you have come to teach them a secret about angles. Do they know that the angles in a triangle always add up to 180 degrees? Use the triangle on your dress to demonstrate (this could be made from material or cardboard). Reveal that Angle A is 50 degrees and Angle B is 65 degrees and Angle C is 65 degrees – they all add up to 180 degrees. Place a triangle on the IWB and reveal two angles, ask the children to work out the third angle. As a class they confirm the answer using a protractor.

Focus of Learning
To understand that the angles in a triangle add up to 180 degrees

- The Angle Angel explains to the children that she has lots of different triangle outfits. She reveals four different types of triangles to the children and explains their different angles. She shows them a right-angled triangle and explains that one angle is always 90 degrees and the other two angles can be any size. She shows them an isosceles triangle and explains that it has two equal angles and two equal-length sides. She shows them an equilateral triangle and explains that all the angles are equal. Finally she shows them a scalene triangle and explains that all the angles are different. She invites the children to play 'Tricky Triangles'.

Using the IWB she shows the children a triangle with one or two angles revealed. The children must work out the missing angle(s) and identify the type of triangle. The children could write their answer on a laminated angel.

- Play 'Travelling Triangles'. Make a set of different giant triangles (on A3 paper). Reveal two angles on the triangle and keep one blank. Make a set of corresponding missing angles and fix each one on a separate bib. Split the class into two groups. Give one group a bib each to wear and ask the children to stand around the classroom or large open space. Place the large triangles face down on the floor. The group without bibs must pick a triangle and try to find their missing angle. Once they have found their angle they must say which type of triangle they think they are. Once everybody has found their missing angle discuss with the children the type of triangle they think they are and deal with any misconceptions.

Practical Activities

- Create some 'Angle Art'. Each child creates a triangle, using a ruler, on a sheet of A4 paper. The children should measure the angles using a protractor. They write the angle in the appropriate place.
- Play 'Angle Angels'. Make a large selection of angels using different triangles. On each angel one of the angles has the correct measurement revealed and one angle is hidden by the angel's head so that it is impossible to measure. The children should use a protractor to measure the second angle. They should then add the two angles together and, using the 180 degrees rule, try to identify the third angle. This could be a timed activity.

- Play 'Actual Angles'. Make lots of sets of angel cards. Each card should display three different angles that total 180. Ask the children to work with a partner. Give each pair a card and ask them to try to draw a triangle by estimating the angles. Afterwards the children must measure their angles and work out how close they were to drawing their triangle correctly. The child whose triangle is the closest receives a point. The object of the game is to acquire as many points as possible.
- Play 'Track Your Triangle'. Make a set of triangle cards with a degree written on and give each child three cards. The object of the game is to collect three triangles that add up to 180 degrees. The children must pass the cards around the circle to the next player simultaneously until one player wins by making 180 degrees.

Art and Display Ideas

- Make moving angels. Place wings at different heights to create different-size angles.
- Create a colour wheel background and on the top overlap triangles to create an angel effect.
- Using Kandinsky's circle work create a similar effect using triangles.
- Using oil pastels ask the children to draw and pastel a triangle picture. Using a silver pen and small pink circles, turn some of the triangles into angels.

Cross-curricular Links

- **D&T** – Make a maze and, learning to measure, mark out and cut angles in wood.
- **Art** – Study the work of Raphael through his paintings of cherubs. Recreate a piece of art inspired by Raphael through observational drawing and sculpture work.

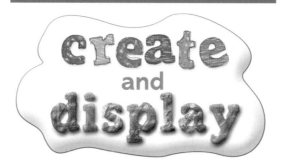

Titles in this series:

ISBN: 978-1-407-11915-1

SBN: 978-1-407-11918-2

ISBN: 978-1-407-11916-8

ISBN: 978-1-407-11917-5

ISBN: 978-1-407-12527-5 (Book)
ISBN: 978-1-407-12533-6 (CD-ROM)

ISBN: 978-1-407-12526-8 (Book)
ISBN: 978-407-12532-9 (CD-ROM)

ISBN: 978-407-12525-1 (Book)
ISBN: 978-407-12531-2 (CD-ROM)

ISBN: 978-407-12528-2 (Book)
ISBN: 978-407-12534-3 (CD-ROM)

ISBN: 978-1-407-12530-5 (Book)
ISBN: 978-407-12536-7 (CD-ROM)

ISBN: 978-1-407-12529-9 (Book)
ISBN: 978-407-12535-0 (CD-ROM)

To find out more, call: **0845 603 9091**
or visit our website **www.scholastic.co.uk**